COLUMBUS
SAILS

CONTENTS

PART THREE: THE SAILOR'S STORY CONTINUED

PART FOUR: SUPPER AT LA RABIDA

Part One :
The Monk's Story

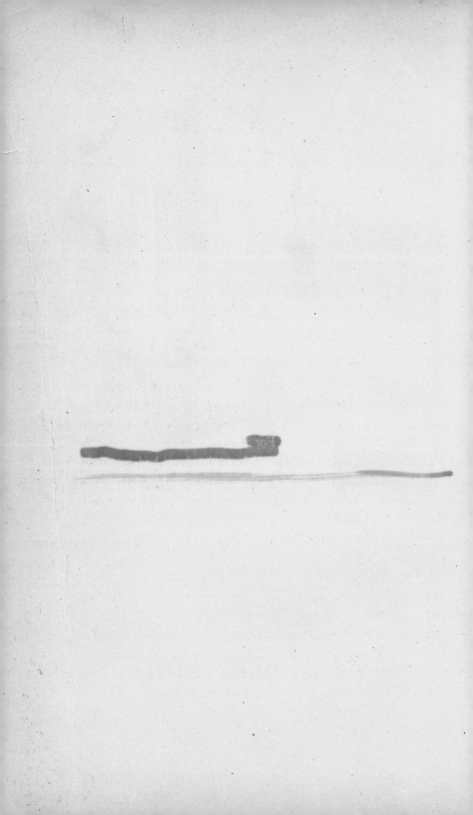

COLUMBUS
SAILS

Written and Illustrated

by

C. WALTER HODGES

COWARD McCANN INC.
NEW YORK

PRINTED IN GREAT BRITAIN BY
BRADFORD AND DICKENS, LONDON, W.C.I

To Rose Dobbs
for perseverance

Contents

CHAPTER ONE

The Map

THIS MONASTERY of La Rabida is built high upon a hill about two miles distant from the port of Palos, in Andalusia; and as I write, sitting in the window of the great library, I can see the town and the harbour, the ships along the quay, and, out to the west, two galleons coming in from the far rich lands of the New World.

From its earliest days La Rabida has been associated with sailors and the sea; and from the time when I, Father Antonio de la Vega, was a young novice here, I have loved the scene I have just described; but in those days no ships came from that far west and none sailed into it. The sailors feared the unknown terrors they believed to lurk there. For the New World had not then been found, and only rumours of fantastic places had ever come over that horizon.

And then there came one man, Christopher Columbus, whose venture found those lands. It is of him I am about to write, for it was at this monastery, and in this library, that his great enterprise first began to bear fruit.

During the year 1491 I was the gate-keeper of our monastery, and every day it was among my duties to give food and drink to such travellers as might seek them. Usually, towards evening, there would be a small crowd of beggars and pilgrims lolling in the porch, talking in low voices as I went round among them. Our Prior, Father Juan Perez de Marchena, would sometimes come out to talk with them, and to give them his blessing.

On the evening of a very hot day, when the hungry at the gate were more numerous and more weary than usual, I saw among them a tall, poorly dressed man, not old although his hair was white, whose general bearing at once impressed me. He was holding a small boy by the hand, and stood rather away from the rest of the crowd. I judged him to be a wandering scholar because of the pouch of papers at his belt. When he and the boy had finished their food and drink, he approached me and asked if they might have water to wash themselves, and I showed them the wash-house on the other side of the yard.

Returning to the gate I found the vagrants had nearly all gone, some to the guest house, some once more upon the road. The Prior had been among them, and now, noticing that I did not close the gate, he asked me why I waited. I told him of the stranger and the boy, whom presently we saw approaching across the yard.

'My son,' said the Prior, when they had come up to us, 'it will soon be dark and it is a rough road outside. The boy looks tired. Would it not be best to stay here for the night? We have room.'

The stranger hesitated at first, but soon he agreed to stay, and continue his journey in the morning. They were going to Huelva, he said; the boy was his son, whom he was taking to live with relations there. The man's speech was quiet and dignified. The Prior asked him his name and his profession.

'My name,' he said, 'is Christopher Columbus, and I am a native of Genoa. I am a sailor and a maker of maps.'

Father Juan Perez looked at him for a moment. Then he smiled.

'Señor Columbus,' he said, 'I have now to be going to the chapel. But since you are a mapmaker I think you would be interested to see our library. Brother Antonio will show you the way, and in a little while I will join you there.'

So I brought Columbus here to the library, his son, whom he

4

called Diego, following solemnly up the stairs. Neither of them said a word until we stood on the threshold, where Columbus stopped and looked about him at the broad maps which were spread everywhere upon the walls and tables, and at the globes of the earth and sky, and the instruments and books of navigation. Then he said, 'But whose work is this?'

'It is the work of the Prior, Father Juan Perez, to whom you have just been speaking,' I replied, 'and of many of the other Fathers. They are all learned students of the art of the sea, and make maps for the sailors of Palos and others who need them. Also they seek to extend our knowledge into the unknown parts of the world. See, here is a map upon which the Prior is now working.'

But Columbus was already bending over it. It was a map showing the western coasts of Europe and Africa and the known islands of the Great Ocean. Our visitor immediately became so absorbed that, when I left him, he was still bent over the table and did not notice my departure. The boy was asleep in the Prior's chair.

＊　　　　＊　　　　＊　　　　＊

So it was that Columbus came to La Rabida. Intending to stay here only for one night he finally remained among us for many months as the guest of Father Juan Perez; for during that evening the Prior had learned the character and aspirations of this man who was to shape the course of the whole future history of Spain and the World. In a few days his story had spread around the brotherhood, and although there were some of us who thought him a little mad, he had a quality of mind that compelled us to respect him.

It is not true to say, as some do, that in those days all men believed the world to be flat, and that the sea poured over the edge of it in an eternal and fathomless cataract; or that the limits of men's knowledge of the world were prescribed by Heaven, and beyond them the Devil lay in wait for the venturesome. True it is that some people believe those legends to this day, despite all that has come about. But they are not of the learned; and even in those days there were many scholars who held the theory that the world is shaped like a globe, and that perhaps somewhere there exist men who walk with their heads downwards (fantastic though it may sound) and their feet towards ours. But it had never been proved. Surrounding us on all sides was mystery, and no mystery was deeper than that of the Atlantic Sea. The farthest islands known to stand in it were the Azores. Beyond them lay the Sea of Darkness, and of the sailors who ventured into it, usually when adverse winds had carried them beyond their course, many never returned and the rest found only emptiness. But there were always rumours, tales of floating islands, of the land of Atlantis, the Islands of St. Brandan and Brazil and Antillia of the Seven Cities. Sometimes, it was said, strange things were washed up on our shores, trees unlike any that we knew, curious weeds, pieces of carved wood. But never any proof.

It was the theory of Columbus that, if the world was round, then he must, by sailing into the West, arrive finally at the lands of India, Cathay, and Zipangu, which Marco Polo and others had described when they returned from the East. The countries of Asia were said to be so rich that the princes roofed their houses with gold, and the people all went dressed in silk and braided their hair with precious stones. The nations of Europe, made poor by constant wars, vied with each other to reach and trade with them. But the way to the East was hard and slow. It took many months for merchants to reach India, many years to reach Cathay and return home again, travelling on camel's back through Tartary, beset by the brigands of the desert and the avalanches of the mountain passes. Therefore the Western peoples strove to find new wealth in lands yet undiscovered, and a new way to the East by sea. And the sailors of Portugal went South along the burning coasts of Africa, hoping always to find their way around the most southerly cape into the Indian Ocean.

Columbus had been many years in Portugal, and it was there that his studies had fired him with his great belief. Since then, for ten years, he had spent his life pursuing his aim, and begging at the courts of kings that he might be provided with ships and money and men for a voyage which would make rich any nation that sponsored it.

He left Portugal after years of fruitless waiting. The King had been interested but sceptical, and too much occupied with the success of his African voyages to give him much heed. So he came to Spain to lay his case before our King Ferdinand and Queen Isabella. Certain noblemen had faith in him, sheltered him and brought him to the court. But the kingdom was at war with the Moors who, for eight hundred years, had invaded and settled in it, and the war, though now nearing its end, needed all the money it could find. There was none to spare for a voyage so speculative as Columbus proposed. None the less his case was submitted to the council; and the council rejected it. Still Columbus did not give up hope. He followed the Court upon its campaigns against the Moors, living as best he could, sometimes making a little money by drawing maps, sometimes living under the patronage of his friends. For six years he waited, and then gave up hope. He would try no more in Spain, but go to the Court of France where, perhaps, he would receive a favourable hearing. First, though, he must take his son, Diego, to the house of a cousin in Huelva, there to be educated and await the better fortune of his father. He was on his way there when he appeared at the gateway of La Rabida, asking for bread and water.

At first he was reserved and said little, a lesson he had learned from his many disappointments; but it was difficult for him to keep long silent upon a subject which had been his life for so many years, and the sympathy of Father Juan Perez soon kindled him to speech. He was a fine speaker, urgent and convincing, and his talk was woven through with a natural poetry. Above all things, I believe, it was the glamour of the enterprise as he saw it in his mind, coloured and pictured like the maps he drew, which, fused with the denials of the Court, had hardened his resolve. And beyond his enthusiasm there was always the logic of his argument.

The Prior, already half-convinced before he ever saw Columbus, was soon converted. But he was too wise a man to trust his judgment where he knew his own theories made him an easy prey. Having many friends among the navigators and scholars of Palos, he determined to seek their opinion. Soon there came to the monastery men like Bartolomeo Roldan and Sebastian Rodriguez, skilled pilots and brave men whose minds were not apt to be swayed by poetry. Columbus and the Prior had long conversations with them.

Then one day there was a knock at the gate and I admitted Martin Alonzo de Pinzon. He was the wealthiest shipowner of Palos, the head of a family of sailors which for generations had been renowned for the success and daring of their expeditions. He was a man of middle height, very broad, and of dark complexion, with a short clipped beard. He was always finely dressed, with gold rings in his ears after the sailor's fashion. His influence was strong in our province, and his shrewdness in matters of the sea everywhere respected. By his coming I knew the Prior had something of importance in mind.

He came often and stayed long, and after these visits Brother Felipe, who waited upon the Prior's table at supper, was hard put to it to satisfy the curiosity of the friars. Through him we learned how Pinzon came gradually to a belief in Columbus's plan and an admiration for the man himself. Thereafter Columbus and Martin Alonzo were often together, comparing charts and drawing up lists for the equipment of imaginary ships. Even young Diego, left to himself, spent much of his time drawing maps upon the

ground and peopling his fantastic continents with stones which, for him, did service as fortresses, cannibals, and sea monsters.

'See, Brother Antonio,' he said to me one day, 'here is Cathay where my father is going. And here is my father's ship; and this is Captain Pinzon sailing along with him.'

For ships he had carved two pieces of wood, and for hours he would steer them past indescribable dangers.

Now, by good fortune, Father Juan Perez had some years previously been confessor to the Queen, and in that office, by the constant wisdom of his advice, he had earned her great respect.

9

She would never deny him audience on any issue. Since his retirement to La Rabida, however, he had never made use of that privilege. Now it was time to do so. Columbus was on his way to France; but before he left Spain his case must be brought once more before the Court, and Father Perez himself would urge it with all the power he could command. This was reported to us by Brother Felipe one afternoon when there were many of us in the cloisters.

'Father Juan Perez has heard news that the King and Queen are with the army besieging the Infidel in Granada. The town cannot long hold out, and with it the Moorish power in Spain will fall for ever, Glory be to God. Father Perez is confident that at such a time Their Majesties will listen favourably to the plans of Señor Columbus.'

'And Captain Pinzon?'

'He, too, is confident. And if the venture receives the Royal Sanction, then he will support it with money, and perhaps with ships. He has promised.'

'Then he will go with Columbus to the Court?'

'No, no, not yet. Neither will Columbus go until Father Perez has spoken with the Queen. The Prior is going alone. He says that he must first prepare the way, and will send for Columbus when the time is ripe. He intends to go soon, though how soon I do not know.'

This question was answered by the Prior himself, who had approached unnoticed.

'Brother Felipe,' he said, 'do not talk so much; and see that my old mule Bianca is well fed; she and I are starting on a journey to-night.'

And shortly after midnight the Prior, alone, with nothing in his pouch but a little bread and a flask of water, set out upon the road to Granada.

10

CHAPTER TWO

Santa Fé

IN THE WEEKS that followed Columbus lived at La Rabida with an ever-increasing impatience, and even before sufficient time had elapsed to make the journey from Palos to Granada and back again, he would go daily to watch the road for the Prior's messenger; or, if he went down to talk with the sailors in the port, he would inquire on his return if the messenger had yet arrived. He often visited Pinzon. Sometimes he would take Diego with him for long walks along the beach.

At last the messenger came. He came very early in the morning and dismounted from his horse in the courtyard just as the friars were passing on their way to Mass. He followed them immediately into the chapel, and Columbus was torn between his own piety and impatience until the end of the service. Not until then was the letter delivered and the seal broken.

It was from the Queen's secretary. Her Majesty, Queen Isabella of Castile, had received the Holy Prior of La Rabida and had heard his appeal. She had assured him of her sympathy and personal interest in the project, and would make every effort to have it brought once more before the Council. To this end she invited Señor Columbus to present himself at the Court, and, hearing of his present poverty, had entrusted her messenger with a purse of money to defray the expenses of the journey and to clothe himself suitably for the occasion.

If Columbus was in any need of further encouragement he

found it in a second letter, from the Prior himself, wherein the details of his conversations with the Queen were set out at length. Father Perez was more confident than ever of success, and urged Columbus to bring with him every detail that he had worked out for the equipment of his voyage. At this last injunction Columbus laughed aloud. For years those figures had never left him. The parchment on which they were written was soft and wrinkled with use.

It was also requested that I, Brother Antonio de la Vega, should accompany Columbus to the Court, having certain private matters for the Prior's attention.

Columbus found a tailor, and completed his other preparations for the journey. As soon as the clothes were ready he said goodbye to his friends, and to his son, whom he was leaving in the care of the monks of La Rabida. Mass was said, and we took the road for Granada.

*   *   *   *

The Royal Standard of Spain had been planted at Santa Fé, a few miles west of Granada, where once had been only a little Moorish village of a few mud houses. During the siege, however, it had been converted into a large fortified town whose streets were trampled all day and all night by the feet of armed men, and churned into furrows by heavy cartwheels. On the outskirts the work of building was still in progress; barracks, kitchens, warehouses, everywhere growing up behind their rigs of scaffolding in the midst of the clustering booths of tradesmen and camp followers. Beyond these the banners of the great nobles floated over the encampments of their soldiers, which stretched far away on all sides. The whole plain of Granada was filled with tents and men and horses, the noise of trumpets and the smoke of campfires. Then abruptly the confusion came to an end where a pali-

12

Christopher Columbus

sade and a deep ditch looked towards the besieged town, about half a mile away. It was calm and silent, without any sign of movement except where the green flag of the Infidel flapped idly on the towers of the Alhambra, the citadel and palace of King Boabdil.

Father Juan Perez greeted us warmly. Columbus, he said, was to lodge in one of the buildings of the Royal Household, under the charge of Alonzo de Quintanilla, the Accountant-General. Quintanilla was one of the few friends Columbus had at Court, and one who firmly believed in the great venture. Another of them was Luiz de Santangel, the treasurer of Aragon. Both these men, hearing that Columbus had come to the camp, were quick to welcome him. But, they said, he must still wait a little before time could be found to consider his petition. The Council was occupied perpetually with the business of the siege. The long trial of patience began again.

Soon after we arrived the Moors made a last desperate sortie, issuing in force from three gates of the town at dawn, riding with loose reins amid a smothering cloud of dust. The alarm was raised, but not in time to prevent them from breaking through the palisades and setting fire to some of our tents. I myself saw King Boabdil storming across the ditch, riding a black horse, shouting his warcry, and tossing his scimitar in the air. His onrush was turned aside and I lost sight of him among the wheeling squadrons of his followers and the smoke. Soon our men had rallied, and the Moors were driven back; but throughout that day there were skirmishes to and fro across the no-man's-land, and in the evening many turbanned prisoners were hanged on gallows erected within view of the walls.

Thereafter King Ferdinand made speedy preparation for a final assault on the town. Columbus wandered like a shadow about the Royal Pavilions at Santa Fé while the captains came and went, very splendid in their armour, and the mounting excitement passed him by unnoticed. This was no time for visionaries. A waggoner, leading a heavy load of cannon stones, might curse him out of the way, and, pressed back among a crowd of kitchen boys and Court followers, a few might recognize him and touch their foreheads with a comic significance; the madman was back again! Sometimes he had a glimpse of the King. A group of nobles would assemble at the gateway of the Royal lodging, the King would come out and mount his horse, and the whole cavalcade would gallop away, banners streaming behind them, trumpets clearing the way, in the direction of the fighting line. That was all.

The masons left the unfinished buildings of Santa Fé and applied themselves to the construction and repair of war engines, which, when finished, were dragged swaying and creaking to the new earthworks which had been thrown up beyond the palisades. Their gaunt silhouettes seemed to overshadow the silent town. But they were needless. Within Granada the people demanded to surrender, and at last Boabdil sent out his herald. The cannons ceased firing and the smoke drifted away thinning into the air.

Thus the warfare of eight hundred years came to an end. A few days later there was assembled beneath the walls of the Alhambra the most splendid pageant of Spanish chivalry that ever had been seen. Every Duke, Count, and Lord of the land was there. Flags, banners and pennants made a fluttering forest of heraldry behind them. In front, mounted on horseback and clad in their robes of state, attended by heralds and trumpeters, the marshals of the royal army, and the princes of Holy Church, under the shadow of the huge embroidered Standard of Castile and Aragon, sat King Ferdinand and Queen Isabella. Somewhere a choir was singing, but not loud enough to drown that faint, thin trumpet note which soon came from behind the walls. Our own trumpets answered with a clamour which echoed and died away among the silent ranks of the army. Then Boabdil appeared. He would not come out to surrender through any of the gates he had striven so proudly to defend. For him alone a breach had been made in the wall, and through this rough gateway he came at a casual pace, riding the same black horse I had seen him ride before, with only a handful of followers. Our Sovereigns received him graciously, and he gave up his sword and the keys of the town. Throughout the army there was no sound until, on the highest tower of the Alhambra the silver crescent on the green ground, the flag of Islam, jerked, dipped, and fluttered down. There was a little pause. Then the red cross of Christendom ran up in its place, and there followed a sound such as I shall never hear again, of cheering and shouting, drums beating, trumpets crying, and joyful salvoes of cannon. The tumult continued unabated for ten minutes, sweeping backwards and forwards over the host like a storm. Then the whole army knelt to pray.

CHAPTER THREE

The Audience

THE TOWN was taken, the Moors were driven out, the wars were at an end. Now, now at last there must be time to hear Columbus. Now at last the victorious Sovereigns would give him ships to sail in quest of his new horizon.

He went to his friend Alonzo de Quintanilla and implored him to obtain audience for him soon. The Accountant-General promised to do so, and on the following day Columbus was summoned into the presence of Their Majesties.

Father Juan Perez, Luiz de Santangel and I went with him to the audience. The antechamber was full of people, little groups talking in low voices, Court officials, men and women with petitions to present. Presently an usher called the name of Columbus, and he went in.

Ferdinand and Isabella were seated on a low dais, surrounded by the councillors and members of the Royal Household. Prominent among them was Fernando de Talavera, recently made Archbishop of Granada, the King's most trusted adviser. Near the dais, a little to one side, was a table at which were seated the Court notaries. There was a subdued light in the room, a feeling of many people gathered in a warm silence. Their dresses seemed to melt into the rich colours of the surrounding tapestries. A blade of sunlight dazzled upon the helmet of a soldier, and its reflection nodded in an opposite corner of the room.

From the table a little man rose halfway to his feet and read from a paper:

'Señor Christopher Columbus of Genoa, making application to Your Majesties for ships to seek out certain lands which he claims to stand yet undiscovered beyond the seas.'

Having gabbled his formality he sat down again. The Queen smiled gently at Columbus and inclined her head towards him. Then the King spoke:

'Señor Columbus is well known to us, I think; but if I remember rightly his proposals were examined by a Special Commission some years ago. Was it not so?'

Columbus bowed, and said:

'At Salamanca, sire.'

'And the Commissioners rejected them,' continued the King, 'on the grounds that you could not bring forward sufficient evidence in support of your theory. Again, was it not so? And was not the Archbishop of Granada here in charge of that Commission?'

Columbus looked across at Talavera, and said nothing. The King continued:

'But since you bring your case again before us, señor, we must presume that you have fresh evidence in support of it. Or that you have fault to find with the method by which it was previously examined.'

'Sire, it is not with the method but with the verdict that I have fault to find,' said Columbus. 'I believe that the members of the Commission were all men of great renown for learning and scientific knowledge. But the greater their learning the greater was their error. They were wrong in their conclusions, and I dispute their verdict.'

'And what says the Archbishop to that?' asked the King. Talavera shrugged.

Queen Isabella

'What can I say, sire, more than Señor Columbus has said? The men whom I assembled numbered among them some of our greatest scholars. Upon my word the hearing was fair and unprejudiced. Señor Columbus has his project much at heart, and it is natural that he should disagree with our findings upon it. Indeed I am sorry. But if he can bring forth further evidence . . .' He was silent. The King looked questioningly at Columbus. 'Can you do that, señor?'

Columbus seemed for a second to be tongue-tied. Then he said, rather slowly:

'I can bring forward a few more traveller's tales, more strange reports; what else had I to do in all these years but to seek and collect them wherever they were to be found? I have no more real proofs than you have heard already. Nor will any man have, until he goes to find them where they exist beyond the horizons of the Ocean itself. Only give me my ships sire, and I will bring you proof enough.'

There was whispering among the company, and someone laughed softly. But the King was obviously impatient. Drumming with his fingers on the arm of his chair, he said:

'We do not doubt your personal sincerity, señor. But you have heard the Archbishop. Without fresh evidence we cannot think it would be justifiable to re-open the inquiry.'

Suddenly the Queen spoke.

'My Lord,' she said, 'perhaps Señor Columbus has not been quite fair to himself. He says he has no further proofs to bring. But since his proposals were first rejected by us he has faced much adversity without foregoing his convictions. Also he has made many friends who believe in him, men whose opinions should carry some weight. If constancy of itself is proof of nothing, at least it has the merit to be heard, even a second time.'

The King looked at her and smiled slightly.

'I stand rebuked, madam,' he said. 'Certainly, if Señor Columbus wishes to speak, he shall be heard.'

Again Columbus bowed; and he began to speak, at first slowly, then with increasing force.

'It is true what I have said. The evidence you have previously examined is still the only evidence I have to offer. But, sire, upon that very evidence I am willing to venture my life. I have shown you maps, drawn up not only by me, but by some of the greatest authorities ever known to have studied the mysteries of the Western Ocean; and I have offered to follow those maps till I have found a way for you across that Ocean to the very shores of the Indies. I repeat, to do so is to venture my life; and not only my life, but the reputation I have spent so much of it to build. I can offer no other guarantee. But if Your Majesties will give me three ships, and accept the hazard, then it must be, if God so wills it, that according to all the known laws of science we shall find those shores that I have promised you, and Spain will become as wealthy as she is now victorious.'

The King interrupted: 'Spain is victorious, but she is also poor. The wars against the Infidel have drained the treasury dry. You say you demand three ships only. But what you really ask is for ships, men, provisions, cannon, ammunition, a thousand things, for a voyage lasting perhaps a year, perhaps even longer. It may be, as you yourself suggest, that I shall never see those ships again. Where is the money to come from?'

'From the Indies, sire!' cried Columbus, 'where there is wealth enough in one province to beggar the combined treasuries of all Europe! This is testified by Marco Polo and Sir John Mandeville, and many other travellers from the East. They have seen kingdoms where swineherds fasten their rags with belts of gold and where the little street boys play in the mud with pearls. They have seen with their own eyes the princes of India riding in proces-

21

sion upon elephants whose thick hides are inset with jewels
patterned like a carpet, whose tusks are carved to the fineness of
lace, and whose ears are hung with bells of silver and gold which
chime with every step in confused and wonderful harmonies! They
say these beasts would seem like gods of splendour were it not
for the splendour of the kings who ride them, under the tinkling
and perfumed canopies that shade them from the sun. Is there
another nation in Europe that would not gamble three ships for
all that treasure? I tell you, for the people who first discover the
Western way to the Indies, a thousand ships will not suffice to
carry home the riches they will find, not even though their holds
are crammed so full they spill upon the decks! All this I offer to
Spain. But there is little time for Spain to choose. My plan is no
secret. It is talked of everywhere, and is plainly written down for
anyone to study. Am I the only man to consider the undertaking?
Perhaps even now in Portugal, or France, or England, they are
preparing ships for just such a voyage as mine. Perhaps in a few
years the Atlantic will be an open road. Perhaps some other man,
not I, will sail the ship that opens it. If this should happen it will
be God's punishment for my pride, for I have lived all these years
dreaming of the pride I should have when I, the first, shall strike
the Spanish flag into the soil of the Indies.

'I have only one thing to add. Upon the floor here between us
is a carpet. It is an Indian carpet such as has great value for us
in Europe. The merchants who trade in such things grow richer
every year. And from whom are they obtained? Not from the
Indians. They are bought from the Moslems of Aleppo and
Alexandria, who alone control the channels of trade with the Far
East. Thus, though you have driven the Infidel out of Spain, you
must still buy in his bazaars and pay the price he asks. And as
your ships return home from the Moslems of Aleppo they may be
plundered and sunk by the Moslem pirates of Barbary, and their

crews sold into slavery. Will you pay that price, and still not grant three ships for a venture such as mine?'

It was plain, long before he finished speaking, that Columbus held the imagination of the Court. Even those who could not believe him to be more than a half-crazy fanatic were moved by the forcefulness of his address. After his concluding words the assembly became aware of its own hesitancy, kept awkwardly silent and waited for the King to establish them again in their former opinions. But the King himself was hesitant. He cleared his throat and looked round at the Archbishop of Granada, and somehow it began to be clear, even from this, that Columbus had made his mark. In a moment the silence was relieved by the mutterings of conversation, and when at last the King spoke it was to make certain the good opinion in which the petitioner now found himself. The King inquired if Columbus had with him the papers and other material relating to the expedition, particularly of the estimated cost. Columbus produced two closely written scrolls, saying that the greater bulk of the material was at his lodging.

'Then, señor,' said the King, 'if you will deliver it this evening to my secretary, I will see that the Council meets to discuss the matter within the next day or two, and I promise that it shall have every consideration.'

More than this Columbus could not have desired. His joy was evident to everyone, and we, his friends, standing in the doorway of the room felt that at last his success was assured.

Our hopes were high. But in a few minutes they were to be brought down even lower than before! Where success had seemed certain, failure became inevitable out of the mouth, as it were, of Columbus himself. For, as we were about to leave the audience, the Archbishop spoke suddenly:

'Señor Columbus has stated his requirements for the expedition,' he said, 'but nothing for himself. Before the matter goes to

23

the Council we should know what reward he proposes to ask for his services. Supposing,' he added, 'that they are fruitful.'

To this the King immediately assented, and the Court again waited for Columbus to speak. After a moment's hesitation he made the following demands:

'Firstly, my lords, I request that I receive a knighthood and the title of First Admiral. Secondly, if the expedition is successful, that I should be accorded the hereditary vice-regency of all the lands I may discover. And thirdly, that I receive a tenth part of all the revenues obtained from them.'

The entire audience was aghast. No one had expected such extravagant demands. When he finished speaking Columbus found himself the centre of a silence so deep that it seemed as though a blanket of deafness had enclosed the room. Not even the voice of anger could find itself. At last the King spoke, quietly, his words magnified by the hush.

'Can you not moderate those terms, señor?'

Columbus spread his hands. 'They are reasonable, my lord,' he said.

'Reasonable indeed!' a thick red-faced man spluttered out suddenly, unable to hold his wrath. 'They are outrageous, monstrous, an insult! Has not this crazy adventurer the wits enough to know his place before the nobility of Spain? What is he but a weaver's son from the gutters of Genoa, and he demands to be made an Admiral and a knight! A peddler of inaccurate maps! He, an Admiral! And since when did tradesmen receive knighthoods? He should be whipped for his impertinence!'

'Sire,' cried Columbus, addressing the King. 'From whom should Spain most proudly accept her Empire: from the hands of a tradesman, or from her own Admiral, duly appointed by the State?'

The King shrugged his shoulders and said:

'Very well, señor. The Council shall consider the matter.'

The Audience was at an end. Columbus bowed and walked quickly from the room. We, his friends, went with him into the bright evening street through the crowd of idle soldiers at the gate. Here we parted company, no one saying a word.

CHAPTER FOUR

The Road to Cordova

THAT COLUMBUS should have asked such high terms had been a shock to all of us, and overweighted by them it was plain that his project would never pass the Council. The rank of First Admiral was among the highest in Spain, and with this and the riches that he might derive from the Indies, if ever he reached them, Columbus's position would equal that of the noblest of Grandees. Small wonder that he had provoked their anger. Yet he would not abate his demands, and we could not even persuade him that he had been rash to make them. His price was fair, he said, and had he asked twice as much it would still be fair in view of what he offered. For a noble venture he asked ennoblement, and, for the rest, only a due portion of whatever harvest he might reap. This was true, indeed, yet he knew that because of it he had failed.

Two evenings later came the Marchioness de Moya, a close friend of the Queen, with an urgent message for Father Perez. The Marchioness was one of Columbus's strongest allies, but brought us the news that the Council had finally declared against him. But even now all hope was not lost, she said. The Queen would still favour him, and the verdict might be reconsidered if only he could be persuaded to abate his terms. It was a faint hope but worth the trying.

The Prior consented to make a last attempt, and, accompanied by myself, hastened at once to Columbus's lodging. We were not

sure whether he had yet heard the news, or whether we should be
the first to announce it.

We found him in the street before the house, dressed for a
journey and packing his few belongings into the saddle-bag of a
lean mule. As we approached him he looked up and waved his
hand to us. He seemed in good spirits.

'I was coming to see you,' he said, 'to say good-bye.'

'But where are you going?' cried the Prior. 'You must not go
– not yet; you must wait a few days.'

'I have waited long enough. I have heard the news, as I see by
your faces you have, and now I am free of Spain. I am going to
France. My friends, I am sorry, and I thank you from the bottom
of my heart for all you have done for me. I know you think that
my own fault has ruined the fair chances you built up for me and,
again, I am sorry. Forgive me. I should never have allowed you
to waste your energies upon my ambitions, but should have gone
to France, as I intended, months ago.' The Prior tried to speak,
but Columbus would not listen. 'No, no, Father, I cannot be
persuaded, not even by you. I am thankful to be going, to be
free of all this anxious antechamber stuff, catching at the sleeves
of so-called influential men, begging to be heard. Perhaps when
I reach France I shall be ready for it again, with fresh zeal. Only
give me your blessing, Father, and let me go.'

There was nothing to be done. He was not to be persuaded.
He knelt in the street while Father Juan Perez blessed him and said
a prayer for his future success. Then he rose, embraced us both,
and mounted his mule.

'And if ever I reach Cathay,' he said, 'I will send you the golden
phœnix bird from the roof of the Grand Cham's palace!'

He laughed and rode away. But as he reached the corner of
the street the Prior suddenly called after him:

'Which way do you go?'

'Through Cordova,' he replied; waving his hand to us he rounded the corner and was gone.

Immediately the Prior turned to me.

'Quick, Brother Antonio,' he said, 'find the Marchioness de Moya and tell her what has happened! I am going to Santangel. Ask her to meet me at his house as soon as she can. Say it is urgent.'

I found the Marchioness still awaiting our return, and expecting to see Columbus with us. Upon hearing the news she hastened to Santangel's house.

Luiz de Santangel had been one of the mainstays of Columbus's cause. He was the wealthy head of a family of merchant princes whose wide experience in commerce had brought him close to the King, who liked and trusted him. With his help, and that of the Marchioness, we might yet save the situation before it was too late. Perhaps the matter could be taken over the heads of the Council. A strong body of Columbus's supporters might be able to persuade the Queen to recall him, with the certainty of patronage, before he had gone too far upon the road to France.

It was a forlorn hope, but the only one. While Columbus was at Court his friends had been content, for the most part, to support him with good wishes and a little money; but now, with his departure, they were brought to realize the true value of their loss, and how they must act to recall it. Santangel lost no time. Within an hour of his hearing the news, some half a dozen of his friends were seated around his table.

Everything depended upon the Queen. In her own right she was sole ruler of the province of Castile, the equal, and not merely the consort, of King Ferdinand. She could, if she chose, act independently of him. If only they could approach her now, this night, while the iron was still hot, and while the sound of Columbus's retreating footsteps could be made almost audible to her, the urgent, ever-pressing background to their arguments, they might persuade her to accept the responsibility.

However, by this time it was past ten o'clock, and the Queen would have withdrawn long ago to her private apartment. Yet delay until morning would be fatal. Here the Marchioness came to the rescue. She would go herself, late as it was, to contrive an immediate interview.

Shortly after her departure the rest of the party cloaked themselves and followed her path through the moonlit streets to the palace. At the Queen's gate they explained to the officer of the watch that they were on State business and were permitted, though reluctantly, to enter the cloistered yard. They waited under glimmering lanterns while a quarter of an hour went by and hope decreased, until the Marchioness came out to them in a flurry of good news.

'The Queen has not yet retired for the night,' she said, 'and has consented to receive you.'

*　　　*　　　*　　　*

Before sunrise next morning a courier wearing the royal arms galloped out of Santa Fé upon the road to Cordova with instructions to overtake Christopher Columbus and summon him at once before the Queen. It was the same messenger who had come for him to La Rabida, but his task was not now so easy, for the highway between Cordova and Santa Fé was crowded with men returning home from the siege. As the sun came over the mountains at the Eastern end of the plain its rays shone pinkly on little plumes of dust kicked up by the feet of companies already on the march. Tents were being folded at the roadside and fires stamped out. Drovers leading their files of laden donkeys turned to whack them into the ditch while the courier galloped past. Flocks of goats, bullock wagons, soldiers, tramps, singly or in

31

groups, there was hardly a mile without them; and, somewhere, any one of them might be Christopher Columbus.

Later in the morning the road became less crowded. The courier ascended the hills to the north-west of the plain, from where one could catch a last distant glimpse of Granada, and entered the mountainous country beyond.

At every inn along the way he stopped among the crowd of drovers to ask if there had been seen a tall white-headed man, riding alone. Once an innkeeper said he thought he remembered such a man, who had passed in the very early morning, before dawn; but he could not be sure, among so many that came that way. The courier galloped on in haste, until the road became too steep for riding and he was for a while obliged to walk. Once in a more lonely place he came upon a solitary mule standing in the road. A few paces to one side a man lay stretched out, half-hidden, in the scrub. He had been slain and robbed, even of his clothes; the night-time victim of bandits. Throughout the morning the tramping companies of the road had passed him by unnoticed. But it was not Columbus. The courier crossed himself and, mounting his horse, rode on.

At midday he drew rein at another inn where an old woman was sure she had seen the man he described. The gentleman had stopped by there three hours before, and she had served him with cheap wine and watered his mule. The courier gave her a piece of money for her news and pressed on downhill. The road became easier and he could travel fast.

After another half an hour of hard riding he came upon a carriage with a broken wheel, and a fine company of people gathered around it. In the shade of a tree some ladies were seated on the ground, while a red-faced gentleman paced up and down in the sun. He was the same man who had raged against Columbus in the court three days previously. His servants and men-at-arms sprawled by the carriage, which had slumped into a pot-hole. The wheel was beyond repair, and someone had gone to find another. The gentleman reported that Columbus had passed by less than an hour ago, and added that it was a good riddance. Showing his royal warrant the courier borrowed a fresh horse from him, and spurred away on his final stage.

Six miles further on Columbus had dismounted by a bridge and was leaning idly upon the parapet watching the steep race of the stream below, when he heard his name called from a distance. Turning, he saw the messenger, who galloped up and drew rein in a smother of dust and pebbles.

'Señor Columbus,' he announced, 'by the Queen's request you are to return with me to the Court. I have her ring as warrant.'

For reply Columbus made a gesture of irritation and mounted his mule.

'Listen, my friend,' he said, 'leave me alone. Go back and say you never found me. I can spare no more time to kick my heels around Santa Fé and wear out my patience waiting for favours from the King of Spain. I have said good-bye, and will not go back.'

He whipped up the mule and would have ridden on, but the courier seized his bridle. 'Don't be a fool, man,' he cried. 'I tell you the thing is yours: ships, knighthood, Admiral, everything you want! Have I ridden after you all this way for nothing?'

Columbus stared at him, incredulous, and he continued:

'Your friends have spoken for you. I don't know what they said or how they said it, but they surely said it well. In short, Queen Isabella has promised you all you have demanded, and she will be as good as her word. It is even said she has vowed to pawn her own jewels to raise the money for your ships. Now will you come with me? Or, if you don't believe me, read this!'

He held out a letter. It was from Luiz de Santangel, and confirmed all that the courier had said. Columbus read it over carefully, studied the seal and the signature, and then looked up and said, mildly enough: 'I can scarce believe it!'

'No more can I,' said the courier. 'But it's true, all right. Well, are you coming?'

Columbus turned his mule without a word, and they rode slowly back towards Santa Fé.

Some way back on the road they met the red-faced man with his party. A new wheel had been fitted to the carriage, which was now jolting slowly along to the discomfort of the ladies who were inside it. The rest of the company was on horseback. As Columbus came up with them the red-faced man stopped his horse and said:

'So you are being taken back, eh? Oh well, perhaps they'll make you court buffoon.'

'On the contrary,' said Columbus. 'It seems they are going to make me an Admiral.'

*   *   *   *

Not long after this it became necessary for me, Brother Antonio de la Vega, to return with the Prior to La Rabida, so that we were unable to witness the final stages of our friend's success. But we knew he was secure. In the last resort the Queen's patronage would break down all other obstacles he might incur and, confident of this, we took our leave of him. We heard from time to time of his gradual acceptance, first by King Ferdinand and thereafter by the Court: how, by slow degrees, his plans matured and were approved in Council; how money was voted and edicts drawn up to equip the expedition; and how all his conditions were granted him without moderation, as we had heard him ask them.

34

And at last we had news that the fleet was to be fitted out in our own port of Palos, and would set sail from there as soon as it was ready. This order was announced by heralds in the town square, one morning early in May, and issued in the name of Don Christopher Columbus, First Admiral of Spain.

Part Two:
The Sailor's Story

Miguel

CHAPTER FIVE

Columbus Sails

In the fort of La Navidad on the island of Hispaniola, in Asia, I, Miguel Pericas of Cadiz, began this narrative on the last day of July in the year of Our Lord, Fourteen Hundred and Ninety-Three.

AS I LIE here, weak from the fever which has not long left me, listening to the sounds of work, the casual voices outside in the sun, and the flies buzzing in the shadows under the thatch, I can think only of the hot summer afternoons at home in Spain, which I may never see again. We live daily in fear that the Indians will attack, and there are but eight of us to hold the fort, eight out of the eight-and-thirty we had when the Admiral sailed in the *Niña* seven long months ago. If he ever succeeded in reaching Spain, we may yet be saved. But it is not to be reckoned on. The appointed time has gone by and he has not returned, while our danger increases day by day. Therefore, I have set out to write an account of our adventures, hoping that some day, even if the worst happens, it may be found and read.

Perhaps you are surprised that I, a common sailor, can write and spell? I admit it is not usual in my trade. Indeed, the last time I put pen to paper was when I signed on for this voyage, and that was over a year ago. But I am what you call 'educated.' My father was a notary. He taught me to read and write and would have made me a notary like himself, if he had had his way. But that was not for me. I think I was the worst son that any man had, and when at last I ran away to sea my father disowned me and, soon after, died. I wonder what he would think of me now, thanking him as I do for the gift of writing?

My reasons for enlisting under Admiral Columbus would take long to tell and have no place here. It is enough to say that while I was in Cadiz I got into trouble. I led a rowdy life, always in one scrape or another, but this time I began to get an unpleasant feeling round my neck and a conviction that it would be better for me to leave Spain as quickly as I could. I had heard that there was an expedition to sail shortly from the neighbouring town of Palos, and it had been given out that whosoever took part in it would be exempt from all lawsuits impending against him until two months after his return. To me at the time this was a godsend, and I set out immediately for Palos. With me came another ne'er-do-well, a Moorish half-breed known simply as Mosca. When he was not at sea he employed himself generally as a thief and a tramp. An outcast since his birth, he had offset this with a fine contempt for everything and everyone, and would do anything for the devil of it. For that last reason he came with me to Palos.

We arrived there in the heat of the day when even the goats by the wayside were dozing, and our first thought was to seek a shady place to do likewise. We found it in a wineshop where we spent every penny we had. True, this was not much, but we were both fairly drunk when, in the late afternoon, we arrived at the place where we had to sign on for the voyage.

Here, outside in the street, there was a crowd of people, mostly sailors by their looks, and a few women along with them. They

were all talking loudly, but what they were saying I didn't notice. The first thing that came into my head was the fear that I might be too late to get a berth, so I elbowed my way to the door, Mosca following me. Nobody seemed to mind. Inside the crowd was jammed close, listening attentively to a spate of thorough sea-faring language from a man up in front. We pushed our way through till we were just behind him. He was over six feet tall, as ugly as he was big, and as powerful as he was ugly. Facing him, on the other side of a long table, was a little hard-looking man, dressed in black, whom I took to be some sort of magistrate. As we came up the big man was thumping the table with his fist so hard that the pen joggled in the inkpot, concluding his speech with the words:

41

'We're not cowards: I'd like to meet the man 'ud dare to say so! But we're not crazy neither! We'll sail under any man that's right in his head, but it ain't in reason to suppose we'll follow some half-wit who wants to lead us all to Old Nick just to find out the colour of his whiskers. No, sir, that's not for us!'

The little magistrate was as calm as a rock.

'It's no use your talking that way, Sancho Gil,' he said. 'You're in this, and you're going to stay in it. And you!' he said, pointing suddenly at us. 'That goes for you too.'

'I don't know what you're talking about,' I said. 'We're from Cadiz. We heard that there was a fleet to sail from here and men were needed. We came to sign on.'

'What?' cried the magistrate, as though we had announced a miracle, and the next moment there was a roar of laughter. Then somebody called, 'Throw 'em out.'

'Silence there!' shouted the magistrate at the top of his voice, and, when the room was a little quieter, 'These two men have more courage than the lot of you put together. Laugh, would you? You ought to be ashamed to look your own women-folk in the face!'

At this the hubbub broke out again louder than before. Sancho Gil, the big man, jumped up on a stool and shouted.

'Lads!' he bawled. 'Don't take any notice of this kind of gab! It's just one of their tricks. These men are nothing but a couple of cheap spies sent in to put up a show to make us feel small. We know what to do with that sort. And I ain't feeling any smaller than I look!' he added, glaring down at us.

At this Mosca flared up. 'A spy, am I?' he shouts, banging on his chest. 'And you're so almighty big! You're so big you think you can tell me what I'm to do! Listen, I just got in from Cadiz to sign up for this voyage, and sign I will, by Jago! And if that don't make you small, I've got other ways!' And here he jumps forward and pulls the stool out from under Sancho's feet. The big man toppled backwards among his friends and landed in a sitting position on the floor.

'Now,' cried Mosca, dancing about like a madman. 'Get up and call me spy again.'

This was going to be the thickest fight I was ever in, I thought. The room was buzzing with anticipation of it. But Sancho just sat there looking rather dazed and surprised.

'Hold Thunder,' he said at last. 'Maybe they're not spies. Maybe they mean what they say.' He got up slowly and stood looking at Mosca in a calculating sort of way. 'Listen, blacka-moor,' he said, 'do you know what you're signing on for? Do you know where you'd be going?'

'No,' said Mosca, 'nor do I care!'

'All right,' says Sancho, 'and I'm not stopping you. Go ahead. Sign.'

By this time there was a crew of officials in the room. One of them brought over a big book and opened it on the table. The little magistrate showed us the smudgy place where we had to sign. Mosca made his mark, and I wrote my name in full, with some pride. I still wasn't quite sober.

When this was done Sancho grinned from ear to ear. Turning to the magistrate he said: 'Now they've signed the book, señor, that binds them same as it does us. That's so, ain't it?'

The little man said it was so. Sancho stopped grinning and turned back to us.

'Now, you couple of beachcombers,' he said, 'you may not be interested, but I think you ought to know where you're going. He pointed across the room to the big window at the far end. 'See all that water out there? That's the Ocean, ain't it? That's what they call the Great Sea, and nobody that ever sailed into it has ever come back. And for a good reason. Nobody ain't ever supposed to go there. That Ocean's a mystery, and it always will be according to the Laws of Heaven. Out beyond there lies the edge of the world where it ain't right that human men go meddling. And there's nothing for them to find there, anyway, unless they're looking for a nice, wet grave.' He paused to let his words sink in. Then he went on in a loud voice: 'All right, then, here's what you don't know. Along comes this Admiral Christopher Columbus that nobody's ever heard of, and he enlists a crew for an expedition. He doesn't say where he's going, but he says we'll find gold, and he offers four months' pay in advance, so all we here sign on. And then what do we find?' He lowered his voice and said in the sort of tone one uses to speak of a lunatic. 'Believe it or not, he says he's going to sail that way, Westwards, to India! India, if you please! When every man with a sound head on his shoulders knows that India lies East, and always will! And that, my lads,' he concluded, 'is the voyage you've signed on for, and I hope you like it. Now perhaps you've sobered up a bit.'

44

We had. It was the most sober moment of our lives. I think the dismay on our faces must have been comic to see, for several people laughed. Meanwhile the magistrate had got the situation in hand. A small company of the town guard had been posted outside in the street, and two men with crossbows had come in unobserved, and were standing at the back of the hall. In the diversion we created nobody had noticed this until the magistrate rapped on the table for attention. In a harsh voice he said:

'Listen to me, men. It won't help you to protest, so you may as well save your breath to cool your porridge. I've been sent here with orders to procure ships and men for this expedition, and I'll do it, whatever the cost.'

A voice called out:

'You haven't got the ships, and you won't get the men either.'

'I'll get all I need,' replied the magistrate. 'Some of the men I have already. That means you, my friends. I will release nobody from his bargain, remember that; every man that's signed will sail. And if I have trouble, then my orders are to hang all who disobey. There will be a roll-call at sunrise and sunset, and if any are found missing the rest will be kept under guard until they sail and their families fined.'

'You can't do that!' roared Sancho. 'When you haven't got a ship, you can't enlist a crew. It ain't sense, and it ain't the law!'

The magistrate smiled drily.

'Truly spoken, Sancho,' he said. 'But we have a ship!'

Immediately there was an uproar. Everyone was talking at once. I was told hurriedly by my neighbour that the shipowners had refused to provide vessels for such a voyage, that ships had been sailed away in the night, for fear government agents should seize them by force, as they had a right to do. And now came this news. At least the crazy Admiral had found one ship. Some old tub, no doubt, a death trap, a floating coffin, some wormy hulk that no one wanted. The men, who knew the points of every vessel on the coast, demanded to know the name.

'And if we're to sail to the devil, don't think we'll do it in a sieve!' someone called out.

The little magistrate became almost affable.

'You can feel easy on that score, lads,' he said. 'She is Pinzon's ship, the *Santa Maria*.'

He had played a trump card, and he knew it. Martin Alonzo de Pinzon was known and respected by all seafaring men in our part of Spain; that he had given his best ship to the enterprise put a spell of amazement over the room. But there was more to follow.

'And that's not all,' shouted the magistrate. 'Here's something else for you to think about. If you're afraid to sail under the Admiral's colours, Señor Pinzon is not. He has been proud to offer his services. Yes, lads, he's going with you. He will himself command a vessel of the fleet. Go home and think it over. If Martin Pinzon can trust him, perhaps the Admiral's not so crazy as you imagine.'

His words had the desired effect. Men started moving slowly for the door. All except Sancho. He stood heavily in his place, scowling and dumbfounded.

'It's a lie,' he growled. 'It's just to get us out of here.'

'Man, you're a fool,' said the magistrate. He held up a scroll. 'If you could read you'd find it on this parchment here. But as it is you'll have to wait till to-morrow when the criers proclaim it officially in the streets. And if I lie, why, you can have your liberty from the voyage, and welcome. All here will witness that I said so. Now go home, and learn your duty.'

Within a few minutes the crowd had dispersed peaceably. Mosca and I were walking towards the harbour with a man who had been next to us in the hall: a grey, quiet old seaman whose name was José Murela. He told us in some detail of the Admiral, the proposed voyage, and the dread with which it was regarded. He himself, he said, was not so fearful.

'I don't care for this business, no more than anyone else,' he said. 'But what of it? A good sailor is nigh to drowning most of his life, and any water'll do for that. That ocean's no different from others, to my thinking. Seafaring men are too superstitious about it. And their womenfolk are worse, so they are. Heads and mouths full of old wives' tales. It's they that stirred up all the trouble this afternoon, and likely they'll do it again. Still, now that Martin Pinzon has declared himself for the Admiral things may go a little smoother.'

We turned a corner and came out on the quay. Fifty yards ahead of us was a ship, moored alongside. José took me by the arm.

'Take a good look at her,' he said, ''tis the *Santa Maria*.'

She was very small, I thought, for such a voyage as this. From stem to stern she measured about eighty feet, a three-masted caravel, rigged with square sails after the latest type. I remembered that I had seen her a few months before, making along the coast below Cadiz, and had admired her then for her grace and beauty. But as she looked now in the evening sun, freshly painted in fine bright colours and flying the Admiral's flag at her mizzen, she made as fine a sight as you could hope to see.

The gangway was ashore. Nearby stood a groom holding two horses. As we came up, a door opened on the *Santa Maria* and two men came out on the quarterdeck. One I knew by sight, the dark weather-beaten man in the rich clothes. It was Pinzon. But the other was more plainly dressed and taller, with a stern, dreaming face and white hair. Before I had time to ask the question José had answered it.

'The Admiral,' he said.

47

They came down the gangplank, mounted their horses and rode away.

✳   ✳   ✳   ✳

The Admiral lodged two miles out of the town at the Monastery of La Rabida, on the hill. But every morning soon after sunrise he was down at the harbour aboard the ship, and throughout the day was to be seen there or at the offices of merchants and port authorities. He was never at rest, and although the Lord knows he often had provocation enough, never outwardly in anger. Delays and frustrations met him at every point, but somehow he overcame them. Captain Pinzon himself went through the town with a drum, enlisting men.

Two more ships had been pressed into the service. These were the caravels *Niña* and *Pinta*, both smaller even than the *Santa Maria*. The *Pinta* was square-rigged; the *Niña* carried lateen sails after the Mediterranean fashion. Now and then their owners would come down to look at them lying in the bay, and to shake their heads over what they called 'their loss.'

Under the Admiral's supervision the supply carts now rumbled hourly upon the quay. Barrels, casks and kegs, sacks of flour, sides of salt pork, bolts of canvas, tackle of all kinds, coils of new rope, oil for the lamps, powder and shot for the cannon, pots for the galley and plate for the cabin table, and bales of coloured stuffs and gewgaws for trading, all were loaded and stowed away. We fitted new gear, new sails. Day after day the work went on.

The morale of the crew had improved, but still was not good; most of us dreaded the voyage. Some deserted, and more might have done but for fear of the gallows which the authorities had set up on the island of Saltes, at the harbour mouth, whereon swung already the bodies of two runaways who had been caught. And we were still short of men. So, as a last resort, convicts were

48

taken from the jails and drafted among the ships. Several of them came with us aboard the *Santa Maria*.

When the company was complete it numbered in all one hundred and twenty men. There were certain gentlemen sent down by the King as government officers to the expedition, and among them was Don Diego de Araña, who came as chief Alguazil. The Admiral himself commanded aboard the *Santa Maria*; Martin Alonzo Pinzon on the *Pinta*, and his brother Vincent on the *Niña*.

We sailed at dawn on Friday the third of August, Fourteen Hundred and Ninety-Two.

＊　　　＊　　　＊　　　＊

The last night ashore was a dismal occasion. The streets and taverns were crowded with people, but few were merry. The town gates were shut and guarded for fear any might desert at the last moment. Through open doorways you could see men who had come home to say good-bye sitting awkwardly among their families, morose and glum.

At midnight the great bell of St. George's Church began to ring. Sailors and townsfolk assembled on the quay where Father Juan Perez, the Prior of La Rabida was to say Mass and offer prayers for the success of the voyage. He came in solemn procession with the Admiral and the captains and all the gentlemen who were to accompany us. The service was long and dim. You could not hear the words, for a stiff breeze was blowing off shore, carrying the Prior's voice away out to sea, where our ships' lanterns were swaying patiently at the anchorage. The chanting of the monks came to an end at last and we knelt for the blessing. Then all became confusion. We crowded to the boats, pushing between the ranks of those taking farewell, more fondly now and perhaps for ever, of their friends. Some of the women were weeping.

50

The harbour was thronged with boats pulling for the ships, and as we drew farther away from the town I thought our spirits rose. No matter where we went, or what happened the die was cast, and nearer with every stroke loomed the *Santa Maria*, alive and tugging at her anchor chain, about to sail. We went aboard and, as we beheld how fine a sight she made that early morning, and heard the wind humming upon the stays and rigging above us, and felt the deck slowly rise and fall beneath our feet, we forgot for a while the dread with which this voyage had haunted us.

'Not long now,' said José, sniffing towards the East, where the horizon showed a faint thin line of dawn. We stood to our stations. The Admiral came aboard, with Prior Juan Perez to wish us all a last godspeed. The sails were down, hanging loose, slapping and billowing, edge to the wind, with a noise like thunder. We manned the windlass, and slowly the anchor warp came in, streaming with water. Standing on the gunwale the old Prior called out his last blessing on us and climbed down into his boat. There was a shout:

'Anchor's aweigh!'

Slowly in the dim light we see the shore turn around to the stern. The sails thunder and tug more violently as though to free themselves; then suddenly they fill, belly out and stiffen. All becomes still. The wind seems to drop as we take up its pace. Looking back we see the curve of our wake and the old Prior standing up in his boat waving to us half a mile away.

By the time the sun came up we were standing well out from the land, with all sails set and banners streaming. Ahead, on the starboard bow, the *Niña* and the *Pinta* pointed our course south-west. Astern lay Palos. The last we saw of it was the gleam of sunshine on the white walls of La Rabida, far away in the distance.

CHAPTER SIX

Grand Canary

'NEARLY EIGHTY leagues,' says Mosca, 'nearly eighty leagues have we gone, and the sun's still shining and the sea's as smooth as a lady's counterpane. And not a finger of the Devil have we seen, not so much of him as would cover a flea!'

'You talk like the fool you are,' said the one-eared sailor. 'We're still in known waters. Down away south, there, lies Grand Canary. But if it's the Devil you wish to see, I don't doubt you'll see him if we hold this course for long.'

This was the fourth day of sailing. Our watch had just come off duty, and several of us were taking it easy in the shade of the foresail. From where I was I could see the *Pinta*, two miles astern, and wondered what made her lag so. The one-eared sailor was splicing rope.

'If we hold this course for long you'll get all the Devil you want,' he affirmed, with untroubled countenance.

'It would be a fine thing, though,' said another, 'if all happens as the Admiral says, and we come romping home to Spain with shirts of gold on our backs, to astonish our women. That'd be worth sailing five hundred leagues to find, Devil or none.'

'Five hundred leagues,' says One-Ear, 'is a long way to go for any kind of shirt. And if we don't touch land before then, it's the mermaids you'll astonish, matey, in the one you have on, dirty as it is.'

'I never saw a mermaid yet,' said Mosca after a while.

'Nor I, for that matter,' replied One-Ear, 'but out where we're heading, they say they're common as porpoises.'

'I'll keep my eyes open for 'em,' said I.

One-Ear spat over the side. 'No need,' he said, 'no need. We'll not get that far. Things'll happen to prevent it, I shouldn't wonder.'

The "Santa Maria"

We were silent for a space.

'Such as what?' I ventured at last.

'Such as the Devil,' said Mosca grinning, 'and all his works.'

'Maybe,' said One-Ear. 'But aside from him there's reefs and tides and hidden rocks, from which the Lord preserve us. And there's things ain't so bad as that,' he went on slowly, 'as doesn't harm neither ship nor crew but sends 'em back to harbour none the less.' He paused to finish off a splice. 'There's a leaky hull, or a split bowsprit; or there's a shift in the cargo, sometimes. All warnings from the Almighty,' he added, 'to deter the foolhardy.'

53

'It's the foolhardy as sometimes get the biggest loot, none the less,' said the sailor who dreamed of the gold shirt.

'And it's the covetous as gets the mermaids,' said One-Ear.

At this moment, gazing astern at the *Pinta*, I saw two little flags run up at her masthead.

'What's amiss on the *Pinta*,' I said. 'She's flying distress signals!'

The "Pinta"

As if to confirm my words, a puff of smoke appeared and faded at the *Pinta's* bow, and the boom of a cannon shot came over the water. We were all on our feet. Men came hurriedly from below, the door of the Admiral's cabin opened, and he came out, a pen still in his hand, and sprang up the ladder on to the poop.

Wondering, I looked quickly across at One-Ear; but his face showed only a nonchalant surprise. We hove to and waited for the *Pinta* to come up with us. The Admiral walked thoughtfully back and forth upon the poop until she was abreast and we could see Martin Pinzon at the rail. Then he hailed her:

'What trouble, there?'

'Rudder,' came Pinzon's voice. 'Unhung. Chain broken.'

'Can't you repair?'

'No good. Must make harbour.'

'Impossible, man!' The Admiral turned away angrily and spoke for a few minutes with Bartolomeo Roldan, the pilot. Meanwhile, the ships rolled nearer together, and communication was easier.

'How did it happen?' called the Admiral.

'I don't know. It was discovered early this morning. I can hold it with a rope, but not for long. We must make port.'

The "Niña"

There was more consultation with Roldan, and the Admiral went below. Presently he returned with his chart, and again hailed.

'How far do we lie from the Canaries, by your reckoning!'

'About four days' sail.'

'With good fortune we'll make it in less. I'll not return to Spain. Alter your course south-south-west and sail on Grand Canary. How long will you need there to make repairs?'

'Maybe a week. I can't say for certain.'

'I'll find another ship,' said the Admiral, 'if I can.'

We signalled the Niña, who all this while had been unable to manœuvre within hail, and we bore away southwards. On the third day the hump of Grand Canary came over the horizon.

We had been only a week beyond sight of land, and many of

Bay of Biscay

SPAIN

Here is danger of capture by the Portuguese.

Lisbon

Palos

out here they lost t of the *Pinta* the storm.

Azores

St Miguel

Sta Maria

Departure
Aug. 1492

Return
March 1493

Santa Maria

Pinta

Canary Is

Gomera

Grand Canary

Part of AF-RICA

The Ocean hereabout was covered thick with weeds.

Niña

A MAP showing the outward and homeward routes taken by
CHRISTOPHER COLUMBUS
and his fleet on the
First Voyage of Discovery.
Drawn by C. Walter Hodges

us had not thought to set foot on it again. Yet here was land at its most beautiful around the blue harbour of Grand Canary; a flowery shore, steep hills shady with olive groves, and the little town standing over its own reflection in the water. Gladly we took in sail and watched the boats rowing out to us and grinned at the chance that had brought us here. That it was an accident, no one believed. The *Pinta* had failed by design, though by whose hand it had been carried out was not discovered; and if the plan had miscarried (for it had not taken us home to Spain) yet it was enough for the moment.

But we reckoned without the Admiral. He would not wait for the *Pinta*. He had said he would take another ship, and since there was none other at Grand Canary he left the *Pinta* there under the charge of Martin Alonzo and sailed away to the neighbouring island of Gomera, where there was reported to be a large vessel awaiting cargo. But here, too, it was the same. The vessel had gone, and the harbour was empty of all but fishing-boats. The Admiral went twice ashore, then in sullen mood he shut himself in his cabin, sent word to Roldan to hoist sail again for Canary, and did not reappear until we were at anchor. Then he ordered that the *Pinta* be hauled up for repair.

I have heard people tell of certain lands where those that visit them are lulled away from the world into a life of hazy luxury, so that they never return again to their homes; and in such a place I thought, were we during those weeks at Grand Canary. We went ashore and made holiday in the sunny town, drank the wine and lay on the sand in the shadow of the vines. Aboard ship we rigged an awning over the deck and the townsfolk rowed out to us with their wares. The *Santa Maria* became a floating bazaar. There were piles of melons in the scuppers, grapes in panniers by the forecastle entry, wine butts upon the hatches, and cages of yellow singing-birds hung around the mast.

Down by the harbour there was a tavern whose name I have forgotten, owned by an old woman called Mama Barba. She was very fat and talkative, and had a chin tufted with hairs. But she did not overcharge for her wine, and her place was popular. On the day the *Pinta* was launched again, there were numbers of us there, sitting upon the clay floor, for she had no benches.

'Launched and all,' said the old woman, filling herself a mug. 'Launched and all! And soon ye'll be sailing. Well, here's to you, me lads, and it's good guzzle, as ye should know. Never did I have such fine customers, never. And ye'll be sailing away for the Grey Islands on the morrow. Such strapping fellows and so far to go, though who knows but you may get there. Ay, ye may so, and ye may come back, even! 'Tis nigh a year since the Islands last was seen, and they come most years, and have done since before I was born. 'Tis far to go, but they may come to meet ye, and Heaven bless ye all for the strappingest lads I ever saw. Here's to ye again.'

'You're drunk, you old witch,' said someone. 'What islands are you babbling of?'

'Why, the Grey Islands. Did ye never hear? No?' She looked around her, incredulous. 'Why, but isn't that your course, into the west? Ay, so it is. Into the west to find the Islands, that's what they told me. There have been some that went before, brave lads, too, and maybe they reached there, maybe ye'll find 'em when ye land; and then ye must seek out one Perillo that was my sweetheart years ago, and tell him I am well and keep good wine. Ay, ay, the Grey Islands, we see 'em plain from here once every year, in the morning and evening when the sun is low, cliffs and hills floating tall and rocky, now clear, now hazy, way out there on the horizon. A strange sight. Then one morning they have gone, and don't come back till next year, sometimes not then. But ye'll find 'em, ye'll catch up with 'em in your good ships. My Perillo went in none like that. So have another drink, lads, at my charge, to speed ye on the way. Bring up ye're mugs! And don't overfill 'em or ye'll run me dry!'

But that drink was not warm for me. Suddenly I had seen this paradise of Grand Canary for what it was – a tiny bead of land upon the fringe of the world, one of a little cluster that stood at the gateway of an unbounded mystery, whose inhabitants gazed daily upon that mystery and breathed it like a vapour. I left the tavern and returned to the ship. For the first time I felt truly afraid of the voyage. Yet when I looked at the ocean it was calm as a meadow, the soft playground of two wheeling flocks of gulls.

We sailed the following noon, and my dread faded for a while. There is nothing raises the spirits like the sailing of a ship in good weather. All was well. The *Pinta* had a new rudder, the *Niña* sails all spread in the light wind. The water was clear as glass and we could see great shoals of coloured fish sweep under our keel, deep down. Grand Canary faded from sight and we drew near to Teneriffe, her peak hidden in a cloud.

Ay, but a cloud of smoke! I did not believe my eyes till others saw it. The mountain streamed with smoke. We gazed in horror, and as we drew closer the sun went down and we saw flames too, glimmering upon the summit and sometimes pouring out in a stream. Upon the side of the mountain red veins appeared like hot blood flowing through the rock. It was a dreadful sight in the dark. Some of us had seen the burning mountains of Etna and Vesuvius, but this, at the edge of desolation and before such a voyage as ours, stood like a terrible candle of warning. The Admiral came out among us and said it was a natural wonder of God, and laughed at us for fearing where we should admire. But I remembered the uncanny nature of these islands, and the old woman in the tavern, and my dread had come alive again and stayed with me till long after Teneriffe had faded in the dark.

By sunrise next morning the little island of Ferro, the last land we should see, was gliding slowly away from us to the south-east. Its steep cliffs and hills were already receding into the distance when the wind, which had been slight, dropped altogether and our sails flagged empty. Ferro stood still. All day we watched it, all night our sails hung useless and next morning it was there still, a little further away, but only a little. It was as though the world held to us, and we to it, by the thread of sight that kept this last lonely island in view. It was as though the world were beckoning us back with this small finger, and we would not come. Then, in the afternoon, clouds gathered over Ferro, and grew black. The island became dark, sharp and clear. The sea ruffled. A wind came down upon us with driving rain, our sails bellied, our prows cut into the waves. Ferro disappeared into the distance and the rain, and we were out, away, gone, alone upon the ocean. The world had driven us forth. High on the poop stood Admiral Columbus, his feet apart, hands gripping the rail, his clothes drenched with rain and his face triumphant.

Rodrigo de Triana

CHAPTER SEVEN

Moonshine

THE WEATHER grew fine again. A following wind drove us westward for days, over a smooth rolling sea. By night the full moon shone with a keen light in which you could see for miles. A narrow beam of it came through the half-open hatchway into the forecastle. The beam swayed slightly to and fro with the rolling of the ship, and picked out the figures of José and the one-eared man, Rodrigo de Triana, and the convict Juan Lopez, wrapped in their blankets. Away in the darkness there were others. The only sound was the slow straining creak, creak of a ship in motion. Suddenly, from above, we heard a cry, and the hollow sound of feet running upon the deck. Then there was silence again for a long while. Presently, the hatchway opened and Sancho Gil came down the ladder.

'What is it?' I asked.

'Something in the water,' he said in a low voice. 'Mendoza was on look-out in the bow, and he saw it and piped up. But it's gone now, gone aft.'

'Let's have it, now it's woke us all,' said Rodrigo, 'what was it? And shut the hatch, for the love o' monkey! I don't like that moon.'

'I came to tell you,' said Sancho. 'It was a ship's mast.'

Rodrigo sat up. 'Out this far?'

'Ay, and been in the water a tidy while, too. All over barnacles it was, and weeds on it like ribbons. No fishing boat's mast neither, but a fine big ship's bigger than this. We'd have been stove in if we'd hit it. It went sloppin' by to starboard, and I thought the *Pinta* 'd have to change course to miss it.'

'Gives you the creeps,' said Rodrigo.

'Why, there now!' said José. 'There ain't nothing strange in driftwood I should hope; it's common enough.'

'O' course it is,' declared Sancho warmly. 'O' course, there's nothing strange in that. But I hope I'm a good Christian and I couldn't help but say an Ave for the souls of them that once sailed under that mast. So I come down for a sup out of my keg to warm me.'

He groped his way back into the shadows and we heard him fumbling among his things. Presently, Juan Lopez spoke:

'It's funny,' he said. 'Bits of wreckage is things you see anywhere. They just float by and you look at 'em and maybe wonder how they came there and don't take no more notice. It's common. But out here, five hundred miles from land and still heading away it don't seem right, somehow. You might expect to see all manner of monsters, but a piece of ordinary flotsam, no. That's uneasy, ain't it?'

'Ye've been at my keg,' said Sancho, coming back and wiping

his mouth, 'or ye wouldn't talk that way.' He sat down at the foot of the ladder. 'This is the natural place to come on wreckage, if what they say is true. Out here is the Ships' Boneyard. They say whenever a vessel burns or sinks or is abandoned, all of it that stays afloat drifts away slowly and is drawn by the sunset into this place. It may take years and years, but they all end up here, sometime. And all that sinks, too, the undertow washes it away, bit by bit, and drags it out here over the sea bottom. And when they gets to the right spot, there they stay, and pile up, big ships and little, rudders, oars and anchors, bits and pieces; and the flotsam mucks together on the top of the water, here a mast, there a hull, all bound together with seaweed till they make a great island that draws like a lodestone. It's common knowledge.'

'Old wives' tales,' said José, 'as usual!'

The Grey Islands, I thought, that float once a year within sight of Grand Canary! Were they not, perhaps, huge grey heaps of slimy wreckage? It was an eerie thought. I asked if anyone here had been at the tavern and heard the story. They had not, and I repeated it to them.

'There you are, ye see,' said José again, 'an old wives' tale, as ye said yerself. Most like she were tipsy, at that.'

Juan Lopez grunted. 'Perhaps they're tipsy in Gomera, then,' said he, 'for I heard the same thing there. Word for word the same. Man, woman and child, they've all seen the islands, but because you haven't seen them with your own eyes, you say it's all wish-wash. Why should your word be better than theirs? Why mightn't it be true?'

'Sure, it's true,' said a voice. It was the Irishman, Herries. He and a few others came forward from the darkness and sat down among us on the boards. 'Sure, it's true,' he said, 'and I can tell you what it is they see. It is St. Brandan's Land.'

The ship lurched suddenly in a big wave, and the hatchway

Sancho

slammed open, letting in a flood of moonlight. We looked up, startled and blinking. Then the ship rolled back and the hatch slowly closed itself. Sancho got up and latched it. We sat in silence until Herries spoke again.

'Near my home on the west coast of Ireland,' he said, 'is the great Abbey of Clonfert that was built by St. Brandan himself when he came back from his voyage. The monks there still have a bit of timber from his boat, and the fishers go to touch it for luck before setting sail in bad weather. St. Brandan lived there nearly a thousand years ago. He and his monks were fishers, living in wattle huts on the hillside, like the folk to-day. The story goes that one day there came a very old man to shelter with him who told him of a wonderful land in the west, far beyond the sea. When he had finished his tale the old man disappeared, and St. Brandan knew it had been a message from God. So he called together his monks and told them the old man's words, and asked who would go with him to find this land. There were fourteen answered him. So together they built a strong boat, rigged it with mast and sail, set up a cross in the prow, and taking with them only bread and water and the word of God, they went out into the ocean.

'They sailed for seven years amid strange and terrible things. They saw burning mountains, and mountains of ice that floated by them groaning. They came to islands where were men that had two heads and spoke no word, and others where men had wings and lion's claws and fed on one another's flesh. They saw monsters in the sea, and a whirlpool so huge that its farther edge lay beyond the horizon and so deep that it gave out smoke. Once they came to a place where the sea was shallow and they thought they were among rocks; but looking down into the water, they saw, not rocks, but great images of the old gods, Fianna and Dagda and Bricciu and Angus Og, Baal and Dagon, hundreds of them standing there for ever, all in stone except their eyes which rolled and flashed under the water. Through these, and many other perils, the Lord guided them safely until they saw at last a grey land in the distance. When they drew near, they saw that it was rich and calm and beautiful, and when they came to shore, they saw trees heavy with fruit and streams of sweet water full of fish, and soft green grass and mossy hills, and birds and butterflies of all colours shining in the sun that never set. Here they stayed and thanked God. But at the end of forty days, an angel came through the glades to meet them and told them they must go back to their own country, and that this happy place should one day belong to their descendants. So they returned home to Ireland at the end of the seventh year.

'St. Brandan did not sail again, but sometimes, in the evening of a calm day, walking upon the hilltop, it is said that he saw his island, like a grey vision, far out to sea. I know this is true, for my own grandfather saw it many times, and my father, too. I ran away from home, fearing I might see it myself.'

'Why were you afraid?' asked someone.

Herries did not reply at once, but tapped thoughtfully with his foot upon the floor. We could hear the ship creaking and the water slapping against its sides.

'Listen!' he said at last. 'One evening, soon after dark, when I was a small boy, my grandfather came and stood in the doorway of our cottage, holding up his right hand like a prophet. "It has come back!" he said. We all knew what he meant. He would often go through the village saying that he had seen St. Brandan's land. But this evening, his eyes were very wide and I was frightened of him. My mother wanted to make him lie down and sleep but he pushed her aside and going over to my father, took him by the shoulder and said: "We have to build a boat, son, big enough for you and me, big enough for all who will come, and we have

67

to sail out to find our Promised Land!" But my father would not listen and the old man cursed him and ran out into the road. We could not stop him. He went to all the neighbours crying out that he must have a boat to lead them to St. Brandan. They told him to go home and sleep. There was a big wind coming up, and the sea was rough and noisy, but still we could hear the old man calling to the whole village to follow him. My father went to bring him in, but he ran away up the hill to the hut where he lived by himself. The next day was so rough that the fishermen could not put to sea, yet one of the boats was gone. Its owner climbed the headland to see if he could spy it, and there, far out, he saw my grandfather sailing away, standing naked in the boat and holding the steering oar in one hand and a cross in the other. He was sailing for St. Brandan's land.'

'Or the Indies,' said someone, 'like the Admiral.'

'Maybe,' replied Herries, slowly. 'He had the fairies in his head. He was mad from the day he was born.'

'And what was the end of him?'

'He was drowned,' said Herries.

Upon the deck someone called the hour, and José got to his feet.

'Time to change watch,' he said, and went slowly up the ladder. The others separated, some to go on deck, some to sleep. The relieved watch came in. I turned over in my bunk and dozed, listening to their talk until they slept. The lamp dimmed, smoked, and went out, and the constant quiet sounds of the ship filled the darkness. Overhead, someone started to sing softly in the night. I knew the song. It was an old sea ballad with a mournful air, and although I could not hear the words, they came quickly to my mind:

> I met a lady on the quay,
> Who hid her face behind a fan.
> ''Twould be a handsome ship,' says she,
> 'That sails with such a fine young man.'

But when I took her hand in mine,
It chilled me cold into the bone.
I stood alone beside the brine,
And in my hand I held a stone.

The voice stopped and did not sing the last verse. But in my
head the words went on:

In calmest night our ship keeled o'er,
And sank into the starry sea.
The waves broke softly on the shore,
And drowned was all our company.

At last my dozing drifted into a shallow sleep. I dreamed, woke,
and then dreamed again. I was in a ship at sea. We were sailing
west, with a steady, following wind. It was broad sunset, yet at
the same time the sky was full of stars, and there was a bright
moon. We went on and on, making good speed, and always it
was sunset, and there was no land in sight. At last the crew became
anxious and decided to turn back. But the moment we put about
the sky became dark, a howling wind bore down on us and huge
waves rose up like walls to bar our progress. In terror we turned
westwards again, and all became still as before, lit by the sunset
and the moon.

This happened many times. We could not return. The wind
bore us ever westwards into the sunset, and there was no land.

All food was gone and we began to starve. One by one we died.

With no hand to guide the rudder, no hand to trim the sail, the
ship still went on before that constant wind. I knew that I, too,
had died. The decks were lifeless. Above, the stars wheeled and
wheeled endlessly in the twilight, years passed, decades grew old;
yet still the ship sailed on in the never-changing sea, always westwards into the sunset.

The ropes rotted and snapped, the sails fell and shredded away.
Our bones became dust. The masts, dry and white and eaten with

69

worms, broke off and powdered into the water. Without mast or sail, the hulk drove on into the west. The years became centuries and still that sunset was empty and the same. The decks crumbled and dropped down, and the hulk became a leaky, slimy, grey, gaping shell that turned and drifted slowly along, always upon the same course.

Countless centuries had passed when there appeared upon the horizon a Shape. By slow degrees it grew larger as the wreck, drawn to it as to the centre of a vortex, circled and circled it and came gradually near. It began to loom and to assume a form in the mist that surrounded it. It had no colour; it was grey. Grey! Grey and massive! Massive and piled up! It was a mountain, a piled up mountain of the bones of grisly old ships that floated on the waves, groaning and whining as though talking to themselves, huge and horrible and dripping, stark, decayed, broken, and slimy with scum and weeds! The boat was close now. It circled no longer, but turned and plunged swiftly towards the dreadful heap. There, upon the prow of the foremost wreck, a shining figure stood with arms outstretched to welcome it. Closer and closer we came, till I could see the face. It was the Admiral!

I awoke with a jerk, sat up in my bunk, and peered into the crowded shadows of the forecastle. The air was close and stifling. Everyone was asleep. I got out and went on deck into the chill. The moon had set and the night was black as pitch, and away on every side I could hear the whispering of the dark and lonely sea.

CHAPTER EIGHT

Day after Day

TWO MORNINGS later came disturbing news. During the previous night it had been observed that the compass was behaving strangely; the needle pointed no longer to the north, but had varied almost five degrees. Could this mean anything but that we had entered at last upon the forbidden region where the laws of nature begin to fail? Uneasily we waited for nightfall; and then, when the north star appeared, it was found that the compass varied more widely than before.

Towards midnight we saw a bolt of fire shoot down and fall into the sea.

Next day, in the early morning, the lookout at the masthead hailed that he saw something in the water far off. It was nothing but a floating mass of weeds, but the Admiral had us change

course slightly so as to bring us into the midst of it. We lowered a net and fished a great heap on board for inspection, but found nothing of interest. An hour later, more weeds were sighted and then more. By evening, the surface of the ocean was blotched all over with mats of scummy green weed which turned in the sunset light to a poisonous brown. We leaned on the bulwarks and watched the stuff until darkness fell; and when I came on deck next morning the weed patches were still floating by, covering the surface in huge slopping meadows, with the sea like lakes between. As the day wore on the weeds grew thicker still, and the stretches of clear water less frequent. As far as the eye could see was a green tangle, and behind us three long paths, like ribbons, showed where our keels had passed.

Rodrigo stood beside me. 'Wind's dropping,' he said.

There had been only a light breeze for the last three days, and now, with the impediment of the weeds, our progress was very slow. I began to wonder what would happen if the wind should fail us altogether. I pictured that green mess winding itself about us, choking us, and clogging all hope of further motion. And what monsters might not come upon us from beneath the slime? Then, even as I wondered, the weeds burst open and two enormous shapes rose up, shining and black, about fifty yards away. They remained on the surface for a few moments, spouted, and plunged below. They were only whales, no cause for alarm.

Later, in the forecastle, Rodrigo drew his knife and cut a notch in one of the beams overhead. There was a long row of notches, one for each sunset since we had left Palos.

'Forty-seven,' said Rodrigo, 'and ten days since we sailed from Canary. By the Admiral's count we have gone four hundred leagues. How much farther does he mean to take us?'

'The point is,' replied Juan Lopez, 'how much farther do we mean to follow?'

These were the first words I had heard spoken which hinted at rebellion. That the spirit was there could not be doubted, but it had hitherto been hidden, hinted at only vaguely, and kept alive between man and man by constant grumbling. But ill-feeling had not formed itself into mutiny mainly because it lacked a leader. Sancho Gil was afraid to trust his great size in any position where it might risk the humiliation of defeat; and he had not the brains of a leader. Rodrigo, although clever enough in stirring up trouble, had not the presence to direct it. But they were both jealous of leadership, and would not have permitted any other to step into the first place, even had anyone presented himself. In the meanwhile the Admiral was well aware of the temper of his crew. He was playing for time; he went among the men, taking personal charge of sailing operations, seemed always in good spirits, and lost no opportunity of pointing out how every sign betokened the nearness of land. Thus, on the following day, when there was a slight rain in the morning, the Admiral pronounced it a sure sign of land, which indeed it sometimes is. He made us fish up another heap of the weed, and this time, among its tangles we found a small live crab. 'How could this be unless land were somewhere near?' cried the Admiral. The mere presence of weed in such abundance was itself a sign. And then, as if to confirm his words, someone suddenly caught sight of a small bird flying low over the surface of the water, and making in the direction of the *Santa Maria*. As we stood watching it, I was reminded of old Noah watching the return of his dove. The bird fluttered around the ship and finally came to rest upon the deck where, for what savage reason I do not know, it was immediately killed. The Admiral sprang down the ladder from the poop and shouldering into the crowd, took the limp bird in his hand.

'Well, lads,' he said. 'Can you want any better proof? This bird is a wagtail. Twenty-five leagues is the farthest distance it can

75

fly from land. Twenty-five leagues! We are on the point of success!'

He waved his hand towards the west, where piled-up banks of cloud had stood like mountains all day. This, too, is often an indication of approaching land. Our confidence rose again. We ran up signals, and the *Niña* and *Pinta* began to close in with us. At the same time, the Admiral gave the order to take soundings, and we let out a line of fifty fathoms.

But we could not touch bottom. And that evening the faltering wind dropped entirely, and we were left becalmed.

The ships were now lying close together, so on the next day, in answer to the Admiral's signal, boats put off from the *Niña* and the *Pinta*, and the two captains came aboard the flagship. For over an hour they remained with the Admiral in the cabin, and in the meanwhile we welcomed their boat crews aboard, like friends from a neighbouring village.

'Perhaps that was not wise,' said old José to me. I asked him what he meant.

'Why, suppose there is mutiny breeding on the *Pinta*? Suppose that the men aboard the *Niña* feel inclined to turn home? Will they not want to know how we feel about it on the flagship? And certainly our friend Rodrigo will lose no time in telling them.' He went up on to the forecastle deck where Rodrigo and Sancho Gil and fat Mendoza and one or two others were talking with some of the visitors. It was as José had said. In covered phrases each crew was seeking to know its neighbour's mind. There was much anxiety. The strange behaviour of the compass had been observed aboard all the ships, and could not be explained. Some said that it was the North Star, and not the needle, which had moved. And now that we were becalmed a new fear had presented itself. What if there never arose a wind to carry us home to Spain? Rumours and apprehensions rose up again, and among them we of the *Santa*

Maria found that by the reckoning of the other two vessels we had sailed much farther than the Admiral had given out. Had he mistaken his calculations, or had he intended to deceive us?

Just before the two captains returned to their ships, one of the *Pinta's* men, a big, lean fellow named Joachim, turned to Sancho and said in a low voice: 'Remember this: we will follow the flagship!'

'And what of Captain Pinzon?' asked Sancho.

'He is a good captain. None the less, we will follow the flagship.'

Sancho winked.

Fortunately for the Admiral, we did not have to wait long for a wind. In the enforced, demoralizing idleness of a prolonged calm he could not have maintained his authority without such stern measures of discipline as he could less and less afford to employ; for the temper of the crews, under the stress of growing anxiety, must soon shake off its silence, and it might be doubtful if he could trust even his officers. However, the wind, when it came was a headwind, strong and steady, a hard wind to work against but an ideal wind to carry us home! Our minds followed it, flying away into our wake, back over the countless barren leagues of water to our own country: while against it, day after day, we sailed on into the emptiness. Our spirits sank into that sulky rebelliousness which was the Admiral's worst enemy. But he had still a cure for it—for the time being.

At midday, he came on deck regularly to take his noontide observations of the sun, after which he gave out orders and announcements. So, on this day, he came forward to the poop rail with Don Diego de Araña at his side and called for attention.

'Lads,' he cried, 'here's something to put the heart back into you if you need it. I've said we were getting near to land; and so we are, make no mistake about it. Any day now, perhaps any hour, and its head will show up over there. You don't need to believe me, you only need to wait and watch. Meanwhile here's this to remember: For the first man among you who sights that land, Their Majesties King Ferdinand and Queen Isabella have promised a yearly income of ten thousand maravedis, until the day he dies. Ten thousand maravedis! To this Don Diego de Arana here will testify upon his office as Chief Alguazil.

'This announcement has been given out to-day on all three ships; and the first to sight land will fire off a gun and hoist all its flags.

'Remember, lads! Keep good watch and keep the guns well primed. We cannot be far off.'

Strange, that ten thousand maravedis could make us believe in land which we had been so sure did not exist. For a while hope revived. We ceased complaining and kept watch with jealous vigilance, fearful, when we went below that land would certainly be sighted during the few hours we were asleep.

So days passed. The sun rose up again and again in the east behind us, overtook and passed us and sank down into the empty sea ahead. The clouds sailed over us, formed and re-formed and cleared away; and others took their place. But nowhere between sea and sky was any sign of land.

Disillusionment

I WAS TAKING my turn at the masthead, crouching in the fighting-top between the shade of the topsail and the wide curve of mainsail, which stretched away below me to where the deck, like a little island, swung slowly to and fro. Down there I could see Jorgé, the Portuguese cook, preparing his eternal fish stew upon the stove; Pepe, the ship's boy, scrubbing out buckets; the Admiral upon the poop in talk with Guttierez; Mosca, standing by the shrouds awaiting his turn to relieve my watch. Away, across a mile of water, were the other ships, the *Pinta* well ahead and the *Niña* abreast of us to starboard, nodding slowly in the waves. Beyond, the ocean stretched away like an enormous wheel whose centre was myself, an expanse without any other feature than the still frequent patches of weed and the shadows of passing clouds. The horizon was level as a knife's edge throughout its whole circle. If only there would appear one single rock to break that flatness! But there was nothing – only the weeds and the cloud patterns, and our little fleet like three chickens that had strayed into a wilderness. Standing there I thought for the thousandth time how remote was the chance that I should ever see any land rise up out of that horizon. I could well imagine the matter-of-fact, magical way in which it *might* occur: but it would not – I knew it would not. I realized that there was not the faintest hope that such a thing could ever happen, that our whole quest was madness. After so long at sea, surely even the Admiral must realize the futility of his undertaking.

And perhaps the most sinister part of it all was the very calmness of the sea itself. It passively accepted our course, it allowed us to go on further and yet further, without storm or hindrance, into its vastness. I had the impression that it was waiting for a time, perhaps not now far off, when we should pass a certain limit beyond which we could have no more hope of return; and there we should perish, inevitably and beyond even the reach of prayer. My dream still haunted me, and I thought: 'It is certain we shall go on like this for ever – unless we turn back now, before it is too late!'

Presently, while I was still in this mood, I heard a noise behind me and looked round to see Mosca's head and shoulders rise over the edge of the fighting-top.

'Your time's over,' he said, as he climbed in, 'and when you go down, there's a rabble want to see you in the forecastle.'

'Who?'

'The big ox Sancho, the one-eared donkey Rodrigo, the fat pig Mendoza and half a dozen sheep. If I was you I'd leave 'em go hang, but it's none of my business.'

'What do they want, then?'

'I didn't ask, but I could stake a guess though. So might you, for that matter. Anything to be seen up here?' he asked, changing the subject.

'Not a thing,' I replied, and began to climb down.

Yes, like Mosca, I could stake a guess at the purpose of that assembly in the forecastle; I could tell it, if from no other source, from the scornful tone of Mosca's announcement. For, as opposition hardened slowly into open revolt, as we proceeded from discontent to the brooding which gathers itself for action, so Mosca had withdrawn from our company. Inwardly he had a sour contempt for all popular opinions. In this voyage he had no more faith than the rest of us; indeed, he hated it. But more strongly he hated our dissension. For himself, he would rather suffer under the strong will of one wrongful man than shout for justice with the multitude. Leave Mosca to himself, then. I reached the deck and made my way to the forecastle which, in this hot weather, was little used except as a storing place. Two or three men sat with their backs to the hatchway, but they moved aside as I approached and let me pass through.

'Shut the hatch,' said Sancho's voice as I entered. I shut it. The place reeked of bilge and sweat, and there must have been about a dozen men cramped together there in the gloom. I asked what they wanted of me.

'Listen, Miguel, you know how to write, don't you?' said Rodrigo's voice.

'Yes,' I answered, puzzled. 'I can do it, if I have pen and paper. But I'm not a merchant's clerk, to be carrying pens aboard with me.'

'The boy can get you all you need when he cleans up in the cabin,' said Rodrigo. 'There's pens enough in there.'

'Even so, what do you want me to do?'

G   81

There was a moment of indecision while everyone waited for the other to speak. Sancho cleared his throat heavily.

'You know what's afoot,' he said. 'Let's have it square, Miguel: Are you for going on with this voyage, or are you for turning back? Are you for sailing this tub till she cracks or do you want to see dry land again? Would you go on with the Admiral, or put about and make for port before the worst befalls us? Which would you do?'

'Turn back,' I said, after a moment; and truly I meant it.

'O'course you would! And so would every man aboard, except only for a fistful; and what should we care for them? There's

enough of us to pitch 'em into the sea if they show trouble.'

'But we ain't playing that kind of game,' Rodrigo broke in. 'It's like this here: the Admiral holds the King's warrant, and we must obey it as near as we can, d'you see? If the Admiral himself gives the order to put about, no man here'll need to suffer for it. We don't want mutiny. But it ain't mutiny if we put our case in writing, telling him fair what we want without open threat. We can leave the paper on his table, without names, so he won't know who's at the back of it. He'll take notice of that.'

'And what if he don't?' Sancho dissented sourly. 'What, him turn back on account of a piece of paper? For love o' monkey, where's your wits, man?'

'He came out here on account of a piece of paper, didn't he?' demanded Rodrigo, 'so what would you do better?'

'You know what I'd do,' said Sancho.

Juan Lopez broke in:

'By the Saints, must we have this again? Rodrigo, you know what it'll come to. It's as much mutiny to show him that paper as to show him your fist. What I say is, give him three days to make up his mind; and then if he don't turn back—'

Voices arose on all sides. Sancho called for quiet, and when it was restored, he said, 'All right, suppose we put it in writing. One way's as good as another. But if he refuses, what then?'

No one replied. Sancho leaned forward. Slowly, a little hesitantly, he said:

'Look at it square, mates. It's the lives of a hundred seamen in danger, for the sake of one man – and him not right in his head! It's his life against ours! You can't deny it.'

Still no reply.

'There's no two ways,' Sancho insisted, 'if he must seek this fairyland of his he must seek it alone. Let him swim for it, say I.'

I stood up and started to make my way over to the ladder. 'You'd best leave me out of this,' I said, 'I'm not having any hand in murder.'

Somebody stood up to bar my exit. 'Let him alone!' cried Rodrigo, and then, to me, 'Sit down, man!' Mendoza, who had hitherto not spoken, exclaimed in his high voice:

'Miguel's right. Murder'll hang us all!'

'Be quiet,' says Rodrigo, 'and listen to me a minute.'

Peace being restored, he went on: 'Murder? For why? There ain't no need. I tell ye, all we have to do, if the Admiral won't heed us, is to lock him in his cabin. He's not the only navigator aboard. We can get back without his help.'

'Ha!' exclaimed Juan Lopez. 'And have him clap us all in

irons when we get there! Have him send us to the galleys!' He lifted and showed his ankles, scarred with the deep marks of shackles. 'Thank'ee, no. I've not long come from there!'

'He won't do that,' said Rodrigo. 'He can't. For who's to bring the charges? Only himself, and there's not a soul else will testify for him. The crew are all on our side, and gentlemen like Diego de Araña may be fine birds among the like of us, but they're very small fish at home. As for the Admiral, I know a bit about him. There's plenty of great noblemen in Spain that'll be all too happy to see him fail, believe me, and they'll see to it he doesn't bring harm to honest seamen like us.'

'What about Pinzon?'

'He's in this for what he can get. And now that he sees there's nothing in it he'll be only too glad to turn back.'

'I wouldn't be so sure of that,' I put in. 'Pinzon's the kind you can't reckon on.' Again in the increasing darkness, the confusion of voices joined from all sides, and argument swelled up. Over all was Sancho's voice insisting upon action, a quick decision, no more delay. Another day of—

'*Almighty! What was that! . . .*'

Like the hand of death, silence came down suddenly. Not a breath was uttered, not a finger stirred. Someone stole cautiously to the hatch and opened it and stood listening. . . .

Again! The sound of cannon! Far off, but not to be mistaken, the thud of gunshot! Shouting on deck, feet running! Quick! Up the ladder! Get out of here! Crowding the hatchway, we bruise our shoulders, our knees, push through into the open. 'The *Pinta*! The *Pinta*! They've sighted land!''

From her three masts, the *Pinta* breaks out her flags. The gunsmoke still hangs like a mist along her side, and from her decks, distantly, comes the sound of cheering. At the high stern, a little figure – it must be Pinzon – gestures wildly to us towards the south-west. Clambering up, clinging to the shrouds, we gaze into the distance, shielding our eyes against the broad, red sunset. And then we see it.

'Land!'

We cheer like madmen and wave our caps. There, there is the land, showing more clearly with every moment of the sinking sun; a low shoreline, a chain of hills and one bluff mountain beyond, waiting in serenity for our approach, standing out now in darker silhouette as the sun touches the water, and darker still as it goes in. Until the last eclipse of the last red fragment of the sun's disc, we watch that constant shore. Then comes the Admiral's voice:

'Men, to the deck! Let us give thanks to God!'

Kneeling on the boards we sang, as with one voice, the 'Gloria in Excelsis.' Then—

'Stand by, lads! Bartolomeo, we'll shorten sail and bring her around close hauled upon the port tack. Make for the land!'

Once more the cheering and then to work, to the squeal of tackle running in the blocks. As night closed in, the fleet was upon its new course. Slowly, cautiously, we advanced, all very quiet now, watching. Upon the thwarts, a man stood sounding our depth. Intermittently through the darkness came the plash of his lead, the long pause, the monotonous cry: 'No bottom yet!'

The night wore on. None slept. Very slowly upon the poop, the Admiral walked back and forth. Sometimes, we talked in low voices, but mostly kept silent, a silence pierced only at intervals by that same cry: 'No bottom yet!'

The night wore on in deeper silence. At last the East lightened and greyness came. Over the sea as daylight grew slowly, so very slowly, a mist, like a web of thin white smoke, rose up. We took in more sail. The voices of command from the other ships came wailing drearily through the fog. The Admiral cupped his hands and called up to the masthead: 'Hola up, there! Anything?' 'Nothing yet, señor!' came the faint answer. And, like a refrain from below, the other cry: 'No bottom yet!'

After an endless while came the sun, and, like a wind, it lifted the mist and swept it back. Even as we watched, the sea grew clear, revealing first our two consort ships, their gunwales lined with men, and then away beyond them until the whole scene stood revealed.

A scene of emptiness. No land, not any sign of it. Only the same perpetual sea, the empty horizon.

We made no sound, no movement, only gazed. Dull, leaden, vacant apathy sat heavily upon our minds and bodies. Like us, the Admiral stood unmoving, and looked upon his desolation. Like us he made no sound. But down his stiff face ran a bright channel of tears.

Then, at last, as if from nowhere, came a voice. Barely more than a whisper, it closed like the bang of a door the last syllable of hope. The voice said:

'It was nothing but the clouds – and the sunset.'

CHAPTER TEN

' *Turn back, Señor !* '

AFTER THIS disillusionment, mutiny was certain; yet it did not immediately raise its hand. Nothing would be easier than to imagine that frustration would goad us to open rebellion, there and then. Instead, it had the contrary effect. Two things appeared. First, as we stood gazing upon that marvellous spectacle of land there could not have been a man in the whole fleet whose imagination was not fired by the wonder of the thing. He, plain Pedro so-and-so, had wrought a prodigy! He, who had lacked faith in the Admiral's new world, was actually beholding it! And even when the apparition had disappeared, there remained for him the memory of his pride. But there was a second and less idealistic motive. Had it been the land, there would have fallen to some sailor on the *Pinta* that reward of ten thousand maravedis. The reward had become real – but not for Pedro so-and-so. And then the vision had dissolved, and Pedro could hope that the reward might yet fall into his lap. By reasons such as these, each man discovered that he had secretly wished to believe in the Admiral's 'fairyland' and now, frustrated, he was prepared to go on a little farther – but only a little – in the hope of bringing it to reality. Thus was the mainspring of insurrection relaxed for a while, and we sailed on into grey, cloudy weather and a sea that was less calm than it had been.

And what is more, for a while, various events contrived to keep our minds upon the bait which still seemed to dangle near our grasp. As I recall it, there were three or four false apparitions of land within as many days. I remember we once saw something that looked like a branch of fruit tangled among the weeds a short way off. Then there were the birds which came suddenly out of the sky, as if from nowhere, to land upon the masts, or swoop by into nowhere again. Mostly these were pelicans, and they came singly; but one evening, we saw a great flock of smaller birds flying towards the south-west. Hailing the Admiral, Pinzon urged strongly that we follow them, since they must be heading for the mainland, and after some deliberation, this was decided upon. We changed our course and sailed on towards the south-west.

But this flow of confidence was of short duration, and soon the ebb set in, a decline which would never stop until it had gathered and risen up in a wave big enough to swamp the Admiral and his Eldorado together. This succession of false hopes was only yeast for the brewing mutiny. Even old José Murela began to feel discouragement eating away his patience.

Meanwhile, backwards and forwards, from port to starboard and back again, and then fore and aft and fore and aft, upon the quarterdeck, walked the Admiral. This had become his habit during long stretches of the day. At other times he would bring out his chair and sit there motionless for hours together, with a rolled chart in his hand, slowly winding it tighter and tighter in his hand, his eyes upon the distance. Then he would spring suddenly to his feet and disappear into the cabin, slamming the door behind him. But he would not stay there long, these days. His anxiety warned him that he must keep his eyes upon his crew as much as upon the horizon. He must not lose this brief hold upon our confidence. But it was all to no purpose. By slow, desperate degrees he saw our shallow-rooted faith drying up, obedience withering into apathy, and discipline relaxing into neglect. He could not enforce it, and had to endure for as long as he could the sight of his ship becoming more and more ill-kept, of decks left too long unswabbed, rope-ends trailing where they should be neatly coiled, of dirty buckets standing in the way, and soiled rags flopped in the scuppers. This was a sign, not of laziness, but of defiance. It was like a dirty gauntlet thrown at the Admiral's feet; and when he stopped to pick it up, accepting the challenge, then the lid would be off and the mutiny out. And he knew it. It remained to be seen how long he could endure.

It was the boy Pepe who flung the last gauntlet, or rather, left it lying for the Admiral to find one afternoon, when he came down into the waist of the ship. The cooking-stove stood uncleaned and sooty, with greasy skillets slopping upon it and the surrounding boards a mess of foul ends and dregs from the unemptied waste-bucket. At the sight of it the Admiral stopped short. From other parts of the deck, the men watched him covertly. Then he turned to Mendoza, who was nearest, sitting with his back against the thwarts, and demanded harshly:

'What is this, a midden? Who left it so?'

''Tis not my business,' said Mendoza, without stirring from his place. 'Pepe didn't clear it.'

'So I see. Then you do so! Get up, there, get to your feet, you lout, don't you know to whom you are speaking?' The Admiral was white with fury. 'Before God!' he shouted, 'Is this my flag-ship, or is it a muck-scow? Clean up that mess and clean it quickly, do you hear?'

Mendoza rose slowly to his feet.

'Not my business,' he repeated, sullenly.

The Admiral drew in one long breath, and struck him with his fist upon the mouth. Mendoza staggered back and supported himself against the stove, covering his mouth with his hand.

'Now clear up that mess!' commanded the Admiral. 'Get down on your knees and clear it.' Dazed, Mendoza went slowly down on his knees. 'Go on! Go on!' Mendoza began to sweep the offal together with his hands, the Admiral directing every move. 'That's right. That's right. Every scrap of it. That bit there, get that up! Over here, here's more! Go on, faster, man, faster, every gob of it, every bit!'

He stood over him until the last scrap of filth had been cleared into the bucket and emptied over the side. Then he turned on his heel and strode away towards the quarterdeck. We stood aside for him to pass. He ascended the ladder and went, more slowly, to his cabin. At the door he turned once to look back at the sullen, confronting faces of his crew. Then he went in.

* * * *

After this, he must have sat waiting, listening for what came at last, after more than an hour of silence – the murmurous swelling up of voices, growing louder and more vehement as the men pushed up the ladders onto the poop where Bartolomeo Roldan stopped them, expostulated, said he would fetch the Admiral to speak with them. From behind the door the Admiral must have heard Roldan's knock, heard him try the latch; but the door was bolted. The Admiral may have been only a foot away, but he did not reply when Roldan called his name. Pedro Guttierez and Diego de Araña had joined Roldan on the poop and were trying, futilely, to silence the increasing clamour; but their voices were drowned down by the shouts of, 'We want the Admiral! Admiral Columbus!' The crowd pressed forward, Roldan and Guttierez still trying to check them, while Diego de Araña, knocking outside the cabin, himself tried to get some answer from within. 'Don Christopher!' he called. 'What shall I say to them?' Out of the throng, Sancho shouted, 'Come on, lads, we'll fetch him out ourselves!' and pushed his way to the front. Others followed him hesitatingly towards where Araña stood facing them beneath the impassive figure of the Holy Virgin carved over the door. 'We will see the Admiral,' said Sancho, 'stand aside, Don Diego!' Araña formed his mouth to say something, but plainly did not know what, and for want of a better answer he shrugged his shoulders. Sancho took a step forward, but before he could reach the door, he found Mosca barring his path.

'Out of the way!' says Sancho and, Mosca not moving, he raised his fist. A dozen voices shouted in contradiction, 'Stand aside there, Mosca!' and 'Let him be!' At the same time, the cabin door opened and the Admiral came slowly forward into the midst.

He stood there, seemingly indifferent, fingering the silver crucifix which hung on a chain around his neck, and holding under his arm a green bundle. Not until the noise had subsided and the last murmur died away, did he open his mouth. Then he said:

'Who is your spokesman?'

Sancho tapped his chest. 'I, señor.'

'The rest of you get back on to the lower deck,' said the Admiral, and waited until the men, after a further moment of hesitation, had moved sullenly down the ladders. When this was done he turned to Sancho. 'Well?' he asked, quietly.

'We are all of a mind, señor,' said Sancho. 'Señor, turn back. We don't wish to make trouble here, but we won't go any further.'

'Your reasons?'

'By St. Jago!' Sancho began to bluster, 'we have reasons enough. This is not a time for arguing. Turn back, señor!'

Don Christopher still fingered his crucifix. 'Since when did an Admiral take orders from his crew? But I will listen to your reasons, if they are good.'

'We don't wish for trouble—' Sancho began again.

'There will be none,' interrupted the Admiral. 'If you will show me good grounds why I should put back, I will do so. If not, do you get down from this deck and return to duty.'

From below there were cries of: 'Speak up, Sancho! Tell him, Sancho! Let him have it!'

'No need!' cried the Admiral, raising his voice suddenly, and addressing the whole company. 'No need. I know your reasons well. We have already gone farther into the ocean than any have dared to do before us, so we are now entitled to return home, to puff ourselves up and tell our friends what brave men we are to have gone at all! That's so, isn't it? Although we shall have done nothing, lacking the courage to hold our path!'

This remark was followed by a storm of angry shouting, silenced again as the Admiral drew the green bundle from under his arm opened and shook it out before the crowd. It was the flag of the expedition, the white cross on a green ground, with the crowned initials of Ferdinand and Isabella.

'This flag was presented to us by our Sovereigns,' he cried, 'and it is the token of their faith in us. Shall we return it to them and say: We failed. Let someone else find the way?'

'The way to nowhere!' somebody shouted. 'We have already come farther than you bargained, and there's nothing here. Turn back, señor!'

'Ay, and we came against our wills in the first place,' shouted Sancho, 'isn't that so, men?'

There was another shout: 'Ay!'

'Don Christopher,' says Sancho, 'if you won't give us the order to turn about, we'll do it ourselves!'

'I will not!' cried the Admiral. 'It is my last word!' An uproar followed, but the men, faced at last with the moment of decision, were still hesitant of taking that final step – force.

'What do you say, lads? Do we turn about?' called Sancho.

'No!' shouted Don Diego, suddenly stepping forward. 'More

time, a little more time!' Then, turning to the Admiral, he said, 'Señor, you must compromise. It is the only chance!'

Juan Lopez called out, 'Three days!' and there was a stir of approval.

'It is the only thing,' urged Don Diego again in a low voice, and Bartolomeo Roldan joined in, at the Admiral's side: 'They are right, Don Christopher. Provisions are running low. We shall have to turn back soon, even at the best. Make terms with them, señor.'

'You too, Bartolomeo?' said the Admiral, 'and what says Guttierez?'

Guttierez shrugged:

'Señor, there seems little else to be done.'

'So you are of a mind. By Heaven!' cried the Admiral, 'what sort of men are you?' Turning to the crew, he said, 'Will you agree to it, then? Give me three days and then if we have not sighted land I will turn back.'

There was a short pause. Then, Rodrigo de Triana, said, 'Ay, it is a good offer, señor. We agree.'

'All of you?' There was a general murmur of 'Ay!'

'And you, Sancho?' Sancho looked round him for a moment, then: 'I agree,' he said, 'if you will take your oath upon it.' There followed a long silence. The Admiral stood fingering his crucifix. At last he said:

'Very well, then, I too, agree. Upon this crucifix I swear that if by the third midnight from to-night we have not sighted land, I will give the order. We will put back to Spain.' Abruptly he walked away and returned to the cabin.

93

CHAPTER ELEVEN

The Ambassador

WE DID NOT see him again all next day which passed without event. After dark, however, towards midnight, he came out and mounted onto the poop, where he stood alone, looking from point to point of all the vague, night-shadowed outlines of his ship and at the distant lanterns of the others. There remained to him but fifty, forty-nine, forty-eight brief hours as commander, and after that he would never have his ships again. Don Christopher Columbus would be no more than the admiral of a dream, the discovery of Vacancy. His life's work was at stake upon a race between Time and Distance. Over and over he must have counted these last few hours, computing their number against the miles that still might lie ahead of us – who should know how many?

He did not leave his post all night save once to fetch his cloak which now, in the keen early morning, clung and flapped about him from head to foot. The wind had freshened to half a gale, and we were making a fine pace, plunging and lifting among the white horses and the grey waves. The decks were chill with spray, the air salty, rope and canvas damp with it. At the stove, Jorgé, the cook, blew and blew on his charcoal to kindle the damp wood, until the smoke started and smothered over the water. He lifted on the soup pots which spilled hissing into the fire with every plunge of the ship. Soon the fishy smell of the soup began to blow in gusts about the deck with the smoke, amidst all the morning

C. WALTER HODGES.

business of sluicing and swabbing, hauling and making trim, until the appetite was keen enough even for this too familiar diet.

Between duties we lined up and Jorgé began to ladle out the hot bowlfuls; but almost too much, even for our hunger and chilled bones, was the sour reek of the soup that morning, when smelt at close quarters.

'Worse every day,' said one, sniffing in his bowl. 'What stuff!'

'Jorgé the poisoner! Whew, the stink of it!'

'We'll hope it tastes better than it smells,' said the Admiral's voice. He had come up unnoticed. 'Give me a bowl of it, Jorgé. At least we can warm our hands on it.' There was some laughter. He took the bowl and went forward up the forecastle ladder on to the prow, where he stood gazing ahead. All had been served, and the soup finished when, suddenly, he turned and hailed back:

'Stand by all hands! Who keeps watch here? Ramon, Lopez, Ibarri, get out the nets, the boathook! José, do you see anything ahead to starboard in the water?'

'No, señor. Ay, now I do, though. But it keeps going awash, and I can't make out what it is. There it is again, now!'

'I can see it!' cries Roldan. 'It looks like the branch of a tree!'

'A branch it is! Look, now it's plain. Have the men ready to bring about. Bartolomeo, we must get it in at all costs.'

'Ho! Helm, there! Ease her a little! Gently, gently! 'Tis too far out, I fear, señor. We'll not get it on this tack and if we come about we may lose sight of it.'

'Bring up as close as you can, then. Needs be we'll send out the boat for it. Look, Bartolomeo, I believe there are still some leaves on it. Can you see?'

'Ay, señor; but not to be certain. Get that boat unlashed, there! José, you'll be in charge; take Sancho, Fernan, Rodrigo. Jump to it! Señor, we're nigh as close as we can make it. Shall we launch?'

'Ay, launch away!'

'Luff your helm, there! Hard over!'

The *Santa Maria* hove to with ruffling canvas, the boat was launched and pulled away. Ten minutes later she returned, slowly manœuvring the flotsam alongside, to be hauled on board. It was, as the Admiral had said, a great branch in full leaf, with berries on it, only recently torn from the tree. How it had come out here was a mystery, perhaps only to be explained by the Admiral's eager face. He said nothing, but plucked off a leafy twig and handed it to the man next to him, as though to say: Let this speak for me. Then, suddenly, Guttierez gave a cry and thrusting his hand among the leaves, pulled out something that had been lodged in a fork there, half-hidden under some winding seaweed. He held it out at arm's length.

It was a staff of wood about three feet long, divided to a narrow fork a few inches from one end, and hollowed throughout like a pipe. What its use might have been was beyond all guessing, but none could doubt that it had been fashioned by the hand of man; for, from end to end, it was banded round with rings of crude ornamental carving whereon there were still some traces of colour.

It was passed from hand to hand. Finally, the Admiral took it and lashed it to the mainmast with a piece of cord.

'It is an ambassador,' he said. 'Let it take the place of honour where all may see it. Even before nightfall, if it so please God, all the great lands of India will be ours. Remember the reward then; and to it I will add my own gift – a jacket of the finest velvet to the first man who sights the shore. Let the watch be doubled. Keep your eyes sharp. Pray to the Holy Virgin and the Saints, and we shall have success!'

CHAPTER TWELVE

Nightfall

MOSCA WAS at the helm. Day had passed, burnt out in a sunset whose last embers were fading bleakly from the sky. Twilight and loneliness gathered in together, deeper than the following night, colder and more silent than the early stars. Immensity came close, cloaked in melancholy. Depth and Distance rocked the ship and were slowly hidden by the darkness. Then the lamps were lit and the world grew small again.

Mosca, watching the compass under the nodding candle, drew his jacket tighter upon his shoulders and steadied the jerking tiller, leaning upon it. The tall figure of the Admiral came up and stood silently by.

'All well, Mosca?' he asked presently.

'Ay, señor.'

'Mosca, on the day of the mutiny, it was you, was it not, who would have defended me? Why did you so?'

'I do not know, señor.'

'Have you faith in my voyage, Mosca?'

'I do not know, señor; I am not one to have opinions.'

'Will you fight, then, for what you do not believe?'

'Señor, I cannot say. That was what happened. I have no beliefs; therefore if I fight I suppose it must be for that reason.'

'Then you cannot have been long at sea, Mosca. A sailor must believe in something, or he will drown.'

Mosca

'I have been a tramp mostly, señor; and when we return to Spain, I shall become a tramp again.'

'Perhaps we are not unlike then,' said the Admiral after a pause. 'When we return, I too, shall be a tramp. I shall have to beg. To-morrow night I must begin to learn the feeling of that. How does it feel, Mosca?'

'It is not bad, señor. But I wish you a better fortune. Maybe we shall sight land.'

'Before to-morrow night? Perhaps. And how will that feel to you?'

'It will be both good and bad, señor. Believe me, there is nothing good that has not its bad shadow. I have no opinions, as I said, but there are certain things I know; and that is one of them. In the end, you might wish that you had become a tramp, like me.'

'You are a gloomy bird, Mosca. I will leave you to your perch. Good night, and keep a good watch.'

'Good night, señor.'

The Admiral moved slowly away into the shadows.

CHAPTER THIRTEEN

Night : The Quarter-Deck

LATER, ABOUT ten o'clock that night, I was standing below the quarter-deck, when I heard the Admiral's voice above me, speaking softly but very sharp:

'Is that you, Pedro?'

'No, señor. It is I, Miguel Pericas.'

'Is Señor Guttierez there? Find him. Tell him I want him very urgently. Hurry!'

I found Guttierez and gave him the message. Surprised, he went up to the quarter-deck, and I returned to my post. Between silences, I could hear their voices, Guttierez' and the Admiral's, but could not make out what they said, until suddenly the Admiral cried:

'There! There it is! D'you see it?'

Then silence again. Some minutes later, the Admiral spoke again, directly above me:

'Are you there still, Miguel? Come here a moment.' I mounted the ladder.

'Have you good eyes, Miguel? What do you see yonder?'

He pointed away over the starboard bow. I followed with my eyes, staring into the blank night. I could see nothing. I strained my eyes till the darkness seemed to dazzle me.

'Do you see anything?'

'No, señor.'

'Look again!'

He seized my shoulder and I thought he was trembling a little. 'It has gone now,' Guttierez said. 'It may have been delusion. It must have been.'

The Admiral made no reply. I continued to stare into the night in the direction he had pointed. From time to time the moon tried to break through the veiling clouds, and by turns the darkness lightened and closed in. But I could find nothing. . . .

'Nothing yet?' asked the Admiral again.

'No, señor. If you will tell me what—'

Suddenly, no bigger than a needle's point, in the far, far distance—

'Yes, señor, yes. Over there! A light!'

A little light, no bigger than a needle's point. It twinkled and went out. 'I saw a light, señor—'

'Hush, not so loud! You are sure? You were not mistaken?'

'I am certain. Look, there it is again!'

It was like a light carried in a small boat on the water. . . . It went out, appeared, went out again. It was like a light carried distantly between trees. . . .

'It is not a star?'

'No, no, a light. I will swear my oath upon it!'

'Why then, Pedro,' said the Admiral to Guttierez, 'we cannot be deceived. But do not mention it to anyone, either of you. We have had too many false hopes. This may be nothing, some will-o'-the-wisp, even some strange kind of fish. Watch and wait!'

CHAPTER FOURTEEN

Night and Morning

'WHAT HOUR is it, Fernan?'

'Almost two, by the glass. Nigh time for us to turn in, thank God.'

'Ay, it's raw cold out here. And I could sleep like a dog.'

'Look at the Old Man, then. Still watching up there like a ghost. Does he never sleep any more?'

'After to-morrow he'll sleep, mark my words. Little we'll see of him 'til we reach port. The poor devil. I wonder—'

The voices came softly out of the darkness near the hatch where I lay sheltered, half dozing, wrapped in a blanket. I could not sleep.

'The clouds are rifting,' said the voice again. 'Looks as if we'll have a moon, after all.'

'Ay, so. She's coming through. More light to see nothing by. Who's aloft this watch?'

'Rodrigo de Triana. With my warm coat on his back, too. The worse luck to him.'

'Well, keep yourself warm thinking of bed. Not long now. And here comes the moon. . . .'

The dim light spread like a film of snow, making everything white. It brightened. Then, from the masthead, came a sudden long cry:

'Land, ho!'

I sprang to my feet. Again:

'Ahoy, below there! Land!'

From the upper deck, the Admiral's voice: 'Masthead ahoy! On what quarter?'

Men came running out on deck. Voices everywhere.

'Starboard bow! Land! Land on the starboard bow!'

The ship's company was all awake, crowding to the side, climbing into the shrouds. About two leagues ahead of us lay a dark streak like a shadow across the sea. Everyone saw it.

'The Indies!'

The covering was stripped from the gun. Powder and shot were rammed home, someone had the match glowing in his hand. 'Wait, not yet!' cried Roldan, but there was no waiting. Boom! and the signal shot flashed into the night.

What if once more we are mistaken . . .? José was on the gunwale paying out the leadline. The clouds were closing again. The streak of shoreline was obscured. Could we be mistaken? Then, José's voice, suddenly:

'Bottom at twenty fathoms!'

No mistake! And as if in confirmation comes an answering cannon shot from the *Pinta*. They too, had seen it.

José called out that the water was steadily becoming shallower, and the Admiral gave the command to come about. We took in all but the squaresail and lay into the wind, awaiting daybreak. The *Pinta* brought up near by, and the Admiral gave her a hail. As soon as her crew heard his voice they began cheering, and the cheering and shouting went back and forth from one ship to the other. Soon the *Niña* came up with us and swung into the wind a short distance astern; and the cheering began again.

There were some hours to wait till dawn. Jorgé busily lit his stove and started preparing food to put some warmth in us. 'What, more soup, Jorgé? Can't ye think of anything else?' laughed somebody.

'He's only got one idea in his head. Fish soup! His brains are

106

made of it. Hey, but stand aside! Bartolomeo's got something better!'

'Give a hand, someone!' came Roldan's voice. He was staggering under the weight of a cask. 'Malaga wine, shipmates! Set it down gently. Steady now!'

'A health to the Admiral!'

'The Admiral! Ay, and the Indies!' cried Mendoza. 'Wealth and fortune for every man of us!'

As for Rodrigo de Triana, he was already planning how he would spend his reward money. 'Out of the lot of you, it was I who sighted land!' he cried. 'There was I at the masthead like a blind priest in a pulpit, couldn't see a thing, and cold as the devil! Then out comes the moon, and there it was! Land! I was near struck dumb, but when I thought of those ten thousand maravedis I found my voice all right!'

Yet I, for my part, was still uneasy, lest we were again deceiving ourselves with an illusion.

'Nay, you needn't fear on that score,' said José. 'This is land beyond a doubt. But what land, I wonder? Will it be India? Cathay? Zipango? What sort of people shall we find when daylight comes? By the Saints, how long it seems till then!'

But dawn came at last. Slowly the night paled from blue to grey, from grey to a mist through which, more and more clearly, appeared the land. As the day brightened there appeared before us the long coastline, a rocky shore where thickets overhung the surf, and in one place a wide beach at the mouth of a river. Northwards, a headland trailed out into the sea; to the south, from among the trees, a thread of smoke ascended into the calm air. Then, the sun came up and lit the whole scene with colour. A flock of birds swerved upwards and from the woods a group of little dark figures ran down onto the shore.

It was the morning of Friday, October the Twelfth, in the year Fourteen Hundred and Ninety-Two.

Part Three :
The Sailor's Story continued

CHAPTER FIFTEEN

The Indies

I write too slowly. Within these last few days our situation here has become so grave that I may not have time to finish this narrative before our end overtakes us. We hardly dare venture from the fort. The woods are full of savages and sometimes, when all else is quiet, we can hear their drums thumping, thumping for long hours at a time. Heaven knows how we shall be able to hold out should they attack in force.

No delay, then. I must continue my story. And where it ceases, if it should break off abruptly with its end untold, pray Reader, for the souls of eight Spanish men at La Navidad.

WE SAILED close in under the land, and dropped anchor. Thus, after seventy-one days our voyage was ended, and we made ready to go ashore.

At about nine o'clock that morning, the Admiral entered his boat. He was dressed in his armour, with a crimson mantle, and carried in his right hand the Royal Standard of Spain. Martin and Vincent Pinzon, each in his own boat, carried the green-and-white ensign of the Expedition. The Admiral gave the sign, and all pulled away for the shore.

As soon as his boat touched ground, the Admiral sprang into the surf and strode up the wide, white sweep of sand. He fell on his knees and kissed the earth. Those who were near him say that he wept. He knelt and prayed silently, and as the boats came in and discharged their crews the men gathered around him and gave thanks to God for having brought them at last to land.

Then he rose up. He called upon us all to witness as he struck the Royal Standard into the ground and took formal possession of this new land, in the name of Their Most Catholic Majesties Ferdinand and Isabella. Thereafter we each took the oath of fealty to him as vice-regent appointed by the Crown.

The whole beach around us was printed with the marks of naked feet. Earlier that morning the natives had come down to the water's edge in great numbers to see the ships. But when the landing parties started out they turned and fled into the woods. The Admiral commanded that no one should venture from the beach until more men had been landed from the ships. Meanwhile, we lit a fire and prepared food. Let the natives make the first move.

Presently we saw two of them among the trees not far off, watching us. We signalled to them to come forward. They made off again, instantly.

'By the Rood!' laughed Martin Pinzon, 'we have mice to deal with!'

Still, there were two of us with arquebuses primed, and all had weapons at hand. It would be unwise to be too confident. Meanwhile we unloaded two chests, containing hawk's bells, beads, bright coloured cloth, and all kinds of trumpery stuff, and spread it invitingly on the beach. Soon there were large numbers of men and women watching us from the edge of the wood.

'Here they come,' muttered Rodrigo, 'as brown as burnt beef and as naked as the day they was born!'

'Don't take any notice of 'em, you fool,' cautioned Roldan. 'Don't look round. Do you want to scare 'em off again?'

The natives were gaining confidence, and some of them had come out onto the beach. One of us, a man named Lucas, with hawk bells tied round his ankles, was dancing a cachucha while others gathered round him in a circle, singing and clapping. Curious to see this and the merchandise we had spread round like bait, the natives now began to come forward.

'By nightfall,' said someone, 'and if we work hard, we may get some of them heathen to scrape acquaintance with us!'

There was laughter. Martin Pinzon took a ball of coloured glass and, after throwing it up and catching it a few times, tossed it into the sand close to the natives, and made no move to retrieve it. After a moment's hesitation, one bold spirit among them darted forward and picked it up. Others gathered round him and the ball was passed from hand to hand amid such a gabbling of wonder as you never heard. Cautioning the rest of us not to move, the Admiral and Pinzon approached them, making signs of friendship. Clearly, they were very afraid, but they did not retreat. I think it must have been the sun, dazzling on his armour, which made them think the Admiral a god. They fell flat on their faces in worship. The devout Admiral was horrified. He raised up the nearest of the trembling, brown figures, and held out to him a little cap of red wool. The man didn't understand. Whereupon,

Pinzon took it from the Admiral, placed it for a moment on his own head, and offered it again. The man took it, inspected it closely, showed it to his neighbours, and solemnly put it on. He looked very ridiculous, but the whole crowd of his countrymen – and there seemed to be hundreds of them now – broke out into cries of admiration.

The rest was easy. In quick succession, the Admiral distributed caps, necklaces, hawk bells and bits of coloured cloth. Within an hour, the beach was dark with people who had come from the villages to see us.

Having recovered from their timidity, they now lost no time in satisfying their curiosity about us. We were submitted to a close and marvelling inspection. Singly or in groups, they approached us to stare, touch, smell and discuss what sort of men we might be. They were especially puzzled about our beards – for they themselves were smooth-faced, every one of them. And so our beards were stroked and touched and even pulled, perhaps to see if they would come off. Under this treatment, Mendoza let out a yelp which made the puller jump three paces backwards in alarm. Next our clothes, and especially our armour, were inspected with much grave and incomprehensible discussion. Not even their obvious respect for the Admiral could save him from this ordeal; but when he drew his sword for them to see, one of them grasped it so firmly by the blade that he cut his hand – and for the second time they all grovelled at his feet in awe at this sign of divinity.

For they knew nothing of iron or steel. Their only weapons appeared to be sticks pointed with fishbones, or, in some cases, sharpened and hardened in the fire. They were very poor and savage. They were without clothes, unless you could call by the name of clothes such strings of feathers, fishes' skins and leaves, and such daubs of black and white paint as they had upon their bodies. Their hair was black, and shiny with fish oil, and was cut

114

Martin Alonzo Pinzon

with a straight fringe across the forehead, the rest hanging long behind them. Some of them had decorated their heads with feathers, parrots' feathers of red, yellow and blue. But those bright colours were the only wealth to be seen in this corner of the far, far East, and, at a glance, did not argue well for the fabled treasures of Cathay.

We saw only one sign, that morning, of the wealth we hoped to find. There were now few women among the crowd, and only one young girl. But around her neck, upon a slender thread, she wore an ornament of shining yellow.

'By Heaven, Christopher,' said Pinzon to the Admiral. 'It's gold, all right, or my name's not Martin Alonzo!'

He signed to the girl to come forward, but she hung back timidly.

'Come now, my pretty,' coaxed Pinzon, grinning a broad, persuasive grin, 'you needn't be afraid of me. I won't eat you. Come closer, beauty, and show us what you've got round your neck.'

He went on like this until, although she couldn't understand his meaning, the friendly tone of his words encouraged her to advance a little, and her friends, in their own barbarous language, urged her on. Very frightened, she approached within arm's length of the smiling captain, who, by way of further encouragement, jovially patted her chin. But this was too much for her. With a little scream, she turned and fled – not, however, before Pinzon had taken hold of the yellow ornament. The thread snapped, and the gold lay gleaming in his hand.

'Well I'll be bilged,' said he. 'A slip of a girl carrying good gold on a thin bit of a string like that! See here, Christopher, pure gold, as I thought!'

But, for a brief moment, the Admiral appeared vexed.

'That was unwise, Martin,' he said. 'We shall not earn their confidence by stealing from them. Here, young señorita!' he called, and threw after the girl a necklace of bright beads. She put it on and went away, seemingly much pleased with the exchange.

Pinzon laughed. 'Well,' he said, 'it appears I didn't do much harm. And as for this' – he held up the gold ornament – 'it is the first contribution of the Indies to the Royal Coffers of Spain. And he placed it with a humorous solemnity, in the Admiral's hand.

*　　*　　*　　*

When we went ashore there had still been a light mist over the land; but as it lifted, the man at the masthead on the *Santa Maria* was able to discern, more and more clearly, that this was an island. He sent word to the Admiral to this effect, with the next boat that went ashore. So this was not the mainland of Asia, and we had still farther to go.

However, such news could no longer shake our confidence. We were sure now that we should find our Cathay, and all day long we made holiday among the groves of this earthly Paradise which Admiral Columbus named San Salvador – The Island of the Holy Saviour.

It was a pleasant country, abounding with fruit and flowers, with streams of fresh water and with laughing hospitality; and the people were simple, and poor in everything but innocence and good nature. They flocked around us all day long, guiding us through the woodland paths, bringing us food, anxious to serve us in every way. But still – this was not Cathay. By signs we tried to find out from them if they knew of other countries near at hand. They replied by pointing away to the south-west.

Just before sunset, the Admiral had Lucas, the trumpeter, to sound the signal for recall. Two miles inland, the villagers of

India heard the trumpet notes of the men of Spain, faintly on the evening breeze.

We had seen two Indian boats, or canoes, as they called them, drawn up among the trees. They were rough-hewn, heavy things, hollowed from the solid trunk of the tree, and we could hardly believe that such vessels could float. But on the following morning, we had much evidence that they could. Soon after sunrise, we saw a little fleet of canoes rounding the northern headland and making for the ships. Later came others from the south. In the remoter parts of the island, the natives had heard of our coming, and were bringing their merchandise to trade with us. We were amazed to see one canoe so large that it must have contained nearly forty persons. They had paddles shaped like spades, with which they made the canoes travel at a great speed, keeping the rhythm with a savage chanting. They came alongside, and it did not take much persuasion to bring them aboard. In a little while, on all three ships, the decks were swarming with Indians and their cargoes of flowers, fruit, shellfish, shrieking parrots and palmetto baskets filled with the white blossom of cotton. The poor heathen thought that our ships were some kind of huge bird from Heaven; that the sails were its wings, and that they had come to trade with gods. They were happy to have whatever we gave them, beads and buttons and bits of glass, even some pieces of broken crockery. The Spaniards got the best of every bargain.

Martin Alonzo came aboard. He had to cut loose three canoes before he had room to bring his own boat alongside.

'How now, Christopher?' he called to the Admiral. 'These sons of Belial swarm so thick on the *Pinta* I came here for refuge. But I see you're as plagued with 'em as I. By the Rood, I'd be better pleased if they'd bring out their gold and leave their parrots at home. I've seen no more of it than hangs at the ends of two or three noses!'

Some of the Indians had arrived on board with small amulets

of gold pierced into their noses. A hawk's bell, a wooden whistle, was sufficient for the exchange.

'Patience, Martin,' said the Admiral, 'there is gold. We shall find it.'

But the Indians, upon questioning, made it plain that there was no gold upon their island. They pointed away westward, indicating that there we should find all we wanted. The Admiral concluded that this must be one of a group of islands lying somewhere off the eastern coast of Zipango. Not far beyond would be India, and, to the north of it, Cathay, land of the Great Khan, of Quinsay, Mangi, Cambalu, richest cities of the world. All these names he repeated many times to the islanders. It may be that he pronounced them wrongly, but they made no sign of understanding.

'None the less, I cannot be wrong,' he said. 'Here lies Asia. Tomorrow we sail again, westwards. The mainland cannot be far off.'

'We could do with guides,' said Martin Alonzo. 'We could do with interpreters. Better take some of our heathen friends along with us.'

But in this, for the first time, we found the Indians unwilling. They were afraid. They gave us to understand that they did not know the way to the west; that they had enemies there who sometimes raided them to slay and enslave. But both the Admiral and Martin Alonzo were fixed upon the need for Indian help, and so, in the presence of the uncomprehending savages, they discussed the plans by which, next morning, nine of their number were to be trapped and carried away, never to return.

Thus, before we sailed, we persuaded some of them to help us take in fresh water for the ships. They came back with us in the boats, came below to stow away the casks. We gave them wine, which they had not tasted before. And we kept them busy. When they were frightened by all the noisy preparation of setting sail, we calmed their fears and gave them more wine. But at the noise of the windlass and of the anchor coming in, one of them, terrified, bolted for the hatchway. 'Keep 'em back!' shouted Roldan, above. But the Indian was too quick for us. We heard him on the deck, calling for help, struggling for his freedom. The others, their eyes wild with fear, were trapped below, bellowing and fighting like a cargo of wild bulls. They were easily overpowered. We had them and we held them. When at last they were permitted to come on deck, it was only to see the farthest headland of the island gliding silently past, over a mile to windward. Even then, one of them made a dash for the rail and was over, before anyone could stop him, swimming for the shore. Whether he made it or not I do not know. The others stood dumbly by the hatchway, watching and closely watched. There were five of them. I believe there were two in each of the other ships. Sadly they watched San Salvador fade away in the distance. The Spaniards were singing a new doggerel:

> The King of Cambalu went down,
> (Santiago was a sailor),
> To see the ladies in the town,
> (Santiago sailed away).
>
> To Selangor and Cambalay,
> (Santiago was a sailor),
> Sailed we on a sunny day
> (Santiago sailed away).

But, alas for the song, it was not a sunny day! It had been raining steadily since early morning, and so it continued, on and off, for the next several days.

*   *   *   *

Hardly had San Salvador sunk below the horizon, when another island came in sight. And then another. I have no time to describe those many islands past which we sailed during the next few days. They were all so alike, fringed with white sand and sparkling surf, and all their hills and valleys thickly covered with palm and spice trees. We were among those islands which, as Marco Polo says in his book, stand in their thousands in the Sea of China. Sometimes they are so close together that the Indians pass from one to another in their canoes, and it was thus that we lost another of our prisoners. A canoe from one of the islands came paddling very near to us, and one of our Indians, seeing it, sprang suddenly from the bulwarks into the sea, and swam towards it, shouting in his own language. The occupants took him into the canoe, and made for the shore. Lopez and some others put out a boat to pursue them, but the Indians outstripped them easily and made off among the trees, leaving the Spaniards with only an empty canoe to bring back to the ship.

A little later, however, it looked as though we would make good our loss. A canoe put out from a distant part of the island, and came towards us. It had a single occupant, a young man who plainly knew nothing of what had just occurred. The moment he was near the ship, some half-dozen Spaniards leapt into the water and dragged him aboard. The poor wretch was limp with terror. He had come to trade with us, bringing as his only wealth, a single head of cotton which he still clutched wet in his hand as he stood shivering before the Admiral. He held it out as a peace offering. Gravely the Admiral took it. Then, in return, he presented the captive with bells, necklaces, cap, armlets, until he was loaded with trinkets; ordered him to be returned to his canoe and set free. The savage returned smiling to his island, and we saw him on the beach flaunting his finery among admiring friends.

For the Admiral, it must be said, had never been whole-hearted in his approval of using forceful methods with the Indians. At San Salvador, not knowing what was to come, he had thought it prudent to take them by whatever means. Now his mood had changed. He was for gentleness and for confidence. Throughout the voyage, he remained of this opinion, while Martin Alonzo and, indeed, most others, inclined more and more to harshness, this mood becoming firmer as our search for gold became more and more frustrated. Thus were planted the seeds of a quarrel which was soon to bring misfortune to us all.

Meanwhile, the Admiral instructed us to treat kindly the four Indians that remained with us. Not that we had ever done otherwise, except in the instance of taking and keeping them prisoners. We fed them well and gave them their liberty on deck whenever we were not too close to land. We gave them names, too, good Christian names, instead of the heathenish babble they used among themselves. Three of them we called Julio, Guapo and Bernardo. The fourth, and youngest, we wished to call José-Maria. But he, strangely, would have none of it. We pointed to them one by one and repeated their new names to them, but when we came to José-Maria, he shook his head decidedly.

'Coatta,' he said.

We repeated very clearly, so that our meaning could not be misunderstood, the name 'José-Maria.'

'Coatta,' he replied, proudly and definitely. And Coatta he remained. Whether that was indeed his name or no we never discovered, but all the time he was with us he answered to no other. And after we had thus accepted him on his own terms, he became the most friendly and helpful of all our Indians. He was the first to speak our language with any fluency, and even before then, could understand and return a sign language which soon made him our chief interpreter.

To teach the Indians Spanish was an amusement with which we passed many tedious hours under sail. They would be together in a group, talking among themselves, we listening. Someone would decide the time ripe for a Spanish lesson.

122

'Spanish,' he would say to them. 'Spanish. Spanish man.'

No answer.

'Spanish man. Spanish men.'

'Spennets men.'

There would be a roar of laughter, in which the Indians joined as loudly as anyone. Then we would try again:

'Ship. Big ship.'

'Tsip.'

'Big ship.'

'Bitsip. Spennets men bitsip.'

This would raise more laughter, and great applause. But Coatta gained the greatest honours one day by coming out with a word, unprompted, but which he had heard often in every mouth aboard.

'Golt,' he said. 'Golt.'

'Gold! That's it! Did you hear that, Sancho? He said Gold!'

'I heard him all right,' said Sancho. 'Ask him where it comes from. Ask him.'

Juan Lopez held up a piece of gold, a nose-ring bartered at San Salvador, and pointed to it.

'Golt,' said Coatta again, beaming.

Lopez pointed ahead, making a question. Coatta looked vaguely, and shrugged. Lopez pointed astern in the same way, and with the same result. We pointed in all directions of the compass, but Coatta did not know. He just shrugged his shoulders and shook his head. Sancho was disgusted.

'Bah!' he said, 'that's what they all say. They don't know. But I say they know well enough how they get it and where they get it. They're hiding it from us, the cunning devils, and they'll never show it to us till we show 'em the lash end of a whip. Take my word for it!'

123

At this moment, we saw the Admiral coming towards us. 'Juan Lopez,' he said, 'I saw gold in your hand. Where is it?'

Taken aback, Lopez showed him the nose-ring.

'You know the orders,' said the Admiral. 'Until the end of the voyage, all such wealth as we find here is the property of the Crown. When we return to Spain you shall each have your share. Until then you will hand it over to me. I'll thank you for this. In future, punishment is for those that disobey. Make it known that I have said so.'

'The old scoundrel,' said Sancho, when he had gone. 'We'll all be beggars when we get home if we don't keep a weather eye open for pickings. All the gold we've found here would hardly fill an eggshell, by Jago!'

CHAPTER SIXTEEN

Kubla Khan

ON FRIDAY, the 19th of October, we arrived at a large island which the natives called Samoet, and which the Admiral renamed Isabella, in honour of the Queen. Here, we were told, there ruled a great king, whose capital was somewhere in the interior. He was very rich, said the Indians. The whole land abounded in gold, and the inhabitants were wont to seek it at night, detecting it as it gleamed in the light of their torches among the pebbles of the beach and the river beds. Our hopes were raised, only to be dashed again when we found no sign of this treasure but only the same poor simplicity as before.

Still, we were not to know. We cruised for a whole day seeking anchorage along a rocky coast, and then, on the day following, hove to off a cape to the north of the island, near a wide lagoon. The wind lay from the land, and all day brought us the scent of flowers.

I was not among the party which went ashore with the Admiral to find the fabled king. Of the events of that day I speak from hearsay, mainly from the account given by Pedro Guttierez.

There was no gold, as I have said. Neither did they find any king. The Admiral's party followed the Indians' paths through the woods which, they said, were fragrant with flowering trees and spices of all kinds, and alive with darting birds.

Their way took them uphill. They marched for two hours without finding any sign of human life, until they came suddenly upon a village. It was deserted. The Indians must have learned of their approach and, strange as it must seem after our welcome wherever else we landed, fled into the woods. There was no sign of them. But their fires were still smouldering on the hearths, and their grain lay half-ground under the stone.

After some indecision, and since the inhabitants did not reappear, they decided to continue on their way. The Admiral led, walking briskly. But they had hardly left the village when a call from Pedro Guttierez brought them to a standstill.

Among the trees, at a little distance from the rest of the village, was a dingy hut. At the door stood Guttierez. He said nothing, but when the Admiral came up, pointed within.

As a rule, the Indian huts are neat and clean. This one was dim with smoke, dirty and foul smelling. The floor was littered with twigs and bones and flat stones laid out in a kind of pattern, and from the ceiling hung down a collection of what appeared to be dead birds and aromatic leaves. By the embers of the fire there crouched an ancient woman, who gazed at them in silence, balefully, and all the time moved her fingers among the ashes, tracing lines.

Coatta was with the party. He could be trusted not to escape, and they had taken him ashore as interpreter. He was told to speak to the old hag, to ask about the king of the island, and the gold.

He seemed to be afraid. He would not enter the hut, but spoke in a low voice from the door. Still the old woman remained silent, and Coatta spoke again. This time she answered, in a little thin voice, and pointed to the west. But this reply, so often given, was no longer enough, and Coatta must question further. What countries were they in the west? What were their names?

The old hag spoke again, and something in her reply caught the Admiral's attention.

'What was that name?' he asked eagerly. 'Speak, Coatta, what was it?'

'Gold country. Cuba. Cubanacan.'

'You hear that, Pedro?' said the Admiral to Guttierez. 'Cubanacan! Listen to that sound. Is it not the name Kubla Khan, but differently pronounced. And is not Cuba, or Cubay, the same as Cathay? We must be almost within touch of the mainland.' He gave the old woman a string of hawk bells and told Coatta to ask her more. But she would not reply again. She sat and shook the bells and inspected them carefully one by one.

'Ask her again,' urged the Admiral, 'how far lies this Cubanacan?'

She still made no answer, and Coatta was pressed forward by the crowd at his back until he stood well within the gloomy interior of the hut. Accidentally his foot scattered the pattern of twigs upon the floor. At that instant the old woman leaped up with startling agility, and let fly a volley of such shrill and heathen gibberish that everyone fell back in astonishment and crossed themselves. Coatta fled in terror and took refuge behind the Admiral, while the old woman continued to screech at him. For a moment no one could do more than gape. Then someone laughed. They left the old witch to her cursing, and, since there was no more to be gained from the deserted village, returned to the shore. And whatever it was the old woman had said, it left Coatta silent and fearful for the rest of the day.

It was getting dark when they reached the boats. The Admiral, intending to speak with Martin Alonzo, had them row for the *Pinta*. As they came alongside they saw an unexpected sight. By the shrouds was an Indian, his arms stretched high over his head, motionless. He had been strung up by his thumbs, able to touch the deck only by the tips of his toes.

The group of sailors, standing near, did not notice the Admiral's boat as it made fast. Their attention was fixed on the tortured islander. Nor did they notice that the Admiral was among them until he spoke.

'Cut him down,' was all he said. He spoke quietly. The men hung back, surprised and awkward. The Indian groaned thinly.

'Cut him down,' repeated the Admiral, louder.

One of them spoke:

'But, señor . . . Captain Pinzon's orders . . .'

'Cut him down, I say,' commanded the Admiral for the third time.

At the same moment Martin Alonzo came forward smiling, from the darkness beyond the lamplight.

'Your pardon, Christopher,' said he, 'it was my doing. Cut him loose, lads.'

'You must be mad, Señor Pinzon,' said the Admiral. 'You know my orders. These people are not to be harmed. What do you think to gain by such foolery, in Heaven's name?'

'Much, my friend. I did not cross the ocean to admire the scenery. Neither did you. I came to seek gold. So did you. So did we all. And thus far we have not been very successful. I think our methods may have been too gentle. Kind words were never a good spade to dig for gold.'

The Admiral pointed to the Indian, who, released, sat huddled on the deck, rocking backwards and forwards in his own shadow.

'And he . . . ?'

Pinzon laughed.

'I am very grateful to him. He has told me something I wanted to know. What have the Indians told you, Christopher? Is there gold on the island?'

The Admiral was silent.

'They told you there was none,' Pinzon went on. 'But I think otherwise. This fellow has a different tale.'

'I don't doubt it,' replied the Admiral. 'Whip him enough and he'll say whatever you wish. You know that, Martin. Besides, we don't need his information, whatever it is. We sail for the mainland to-morrow.'

'We haven't been here two days yet,' said Pinzon.

'And what of that?'

Pinzon took him by the arm. 'Come, Christopher,' he said, 'it isn't for myself. It's for the men. They're beginning to grumble. You can understand that. We promised them riches, and must give them opportunity to find them. We must stay here until we've tried the truth of what this fellow says. We'll find gold in this place if we have to dig up their houses for it. Only say the word, and we'll do it.'

The Admiral shook himself free.

'I didn't think you were simple, Señor Pinzon,' said he, and walked to the rail. With one foot over the side, he turned again. 'We sail to-morrow. At sunrise. Is that understood?'

Pinzon made to reply, checked himself, and stood silent and grim-faced. Then:

'It is clearly understood, señor,' he said in a low voice.

Next morning, the fleet weighed anchor and stood off west-sou'-west in the direction of Cuba.

CHAPTER SEVENTEEN

Martin Alonzo sets a Course

THIS WAS the first we heard of the quarrel between the Admiral
and his chief lieutenant; but it was not the beginning. It had
really begun from the moment when the Indies came first in view.
Standing on his quarterdeck, Don Christopher Columbus gazed
upon that shore, and knew that he had won. Year after year
he had fought his battle alone, and his only reward had been the
laughter of people who thought him mad. His mission had
been scorned wherever he had proclaimed it; learned men had
refuted it, but he had held on. And when at last he had got his

ships, he found himself faced with mutiny and little faith. Scorn, coolness, discouragement, mutiny, he had beaten them all. He had won. Here was his victory. If his resolution had been hard before, it was harder now. Since he was proven to be right, he need no longer pay heed to any other judgment than his own. And of all that he had discovered and still was to discover he was, by Royal Charter, the Viceroy. He would be the richest and the most renowned man in all Spain, and through him, Spain would become the richest and most powerful nation in the world.

Such must have been his thoughts that morning. As the days went by, it became noticeable that his manner had changed. His commands endured no compromise. Plainly, it made no difference to him whether we found much gold or little, or whether we returned to Spain as poor as we had left.

But Martin Alonzo Pinzon was a merchant adventurer, and that only. He had not ventured his life, his money or his ships for the pursuit of an ideal. A voyage must pay its way or it was a wasted voyage. And he resented bitterly the Admiral's new dictatorial tone. Perhaps he felt that it was due to his own assistance that the enterprise had succeeded. Certainly it was partly due to it. And there was his pride, too. He was head of a family famous for generations in Andalusia. No sailor but was proud to sail under the flag of Pinzon. Yet here he had been rapped over the knuckles by a Genoese adventurer who was lording it in new-found honours, and aboard his, Pinzon's, own ship. 'I did not think you were so simple, Señor Pinzon,' Columbus had said. During the four days' voyage to Cuba, Pinzon followed the Admiral's ship, made no signals, and nursed his resentment.

For five weeks we explored the coast of Cuba, back and forth, and during all that time found not one sign of the cities, government and commerce that we had so confidently expected. More strange, we met none of those great ships, trading for the Khan which are known to ply the coast of Asia. It was always the same tale of primitives with their canoes, of simple palm-thatched dwellings, and reports of treasure, yes, much treasure—farther on! At one place we did find examples of crude art, carved idols of men and women, which perhaps the people worship, to their shame. But they were in stone and wood, and of no value.

Yet it is not to be doubted that this was the mainland of Asia. Had we gone further, and not turned back as we did, on the 12th of November, we must surely have reached the kingdom of Cathay.

Meanwhile we sailed uncertainly, in changeable weather. First there were heavy storms of rain; then it grew very hot, and the wind fell off. Thunder clouds shrouded the inland mountains, and rumbled throughout the day. Tempers wore thin among the crews, and quarrels were frequent. A petty theft, a lost game, a word, would be enough for the start. The Indians – there were many with us now – watched, and were not moved; and sometimes quarrelled among themselves.

The ships were very foul with weed. At a river mouth, at a place we called Rio de los Mares, where there was a good beach, we took them ashore and careened them. And while this was doing, the Admiral sent an expedition into the interior with Indian guides, who professed to be able to lead them to the Khan. José Murela went, and two others named Rodrigo de Jerez and Luiz de Torres; the latter was a converted Jew, who knew Hebrew and Chaldean and a little Arabic, one or the other of which Columbus supposed might be known to this oriental prince. They were gone six days, and returned, as usual, empty handed.

During all this time we had seen very little of Martin Alonzo. His breach with the Admiral did not heal, but grew more dangerous with every meeting. So he remained in his own ship and kept his own counsel. Then one day, when we had got under sail again and were making hard going with contrary winds, he came aboard.

To my mind, he had chosen a bad time for it, for the Admiral was short of temper that morning. Shortly before, he had found the helm in charge of the ship's boy, Pepe. He was ambitious to know the sea, was Pepe, and had picked up bits and pieces of the sailor's craft from one person and another throughout the voyage. To-day was Sancho's trick at the helm, and under persuasion, he had let Pepe take over, at a time when the Admiral was not usually on deck. True, Sancho had stayed near the boy so that nothing could go wrong, but, needless to say, this would not excuse it. And the Admiral, coming unexpectedly from his cabin, broke into a fury.

He rated Sancho first, and then the entire crew, for slackness and indiscipline. That a ship like this, on such an enterprise, should be left so hazardously in the hands of an untrained boy! And he was right, as events proved later. Meanwhile, it was at this moment that the look-out reported Martin Alonzo coming alongside in the small boat.

From the moment he stepped aboard it was plain that he meant to be amiable. He chatted for a few minutes with several of the crew, without appearing to notice that the Admiral was on deck; and it may be that the Admiral, already angry, took it as an intended slight. It was as though Martin Alonzo had said, 'These are Palos men, *my* men, who have known me and worked for me all their lives. And you they have known these four months only.' I do not think it was so meant. None the less, the Admiral did not go up to greet his captain, but waited until the latter himself had noticed and, with a quick apology, approached him.

'Forgive me, Christopher,' said he, 'I had not seen you here.' And then, clapping his arm round the other's shoulder, with a bluff, familiar air: 'My friend, I have news. An island called Babeque. My Indians say it lies within easy sail, eastwards. From their account I make it to be about sixty miles from here. And they are certain we shall find spices and gold in such quantity as to make it well worth altering our course. They all agree about the place. I have never known 'em so sure, in fact.'

'A familiar story,' said the Admiral.

'Of course, of course. But I have a feeling about it. It might repay us well. Besides – but I will show you on the map. Shall we go to the cabin?'

Some twenty minutes later we heard angry voices from the cabin, first Pinzon and then the Admiral.

The careful Bartolomeo Roldan tried to keep the crew beyond earshot of the quarrel, but from the steersman's post, which is directly beneath the cabin, Sancho could hear almost every word. It seems that the Admiral refused to change his course to pursue yet another Indian fancy. He had his own plans to follow. Pinzon could not move him, and grew heated.

'And what will you say to them in Spain,' he demanded suddenly, 'when you return with nothing in your hold but a parcel of brown savages and a handful of cinnamon? Man, you are not your own master here. You serve the King, and have an account to render. He will ask you where is the treasure you promised him, and what will you say?'

'Let that be my affair,' says the Admiral, meaning – and keep you to yours. Whereupon Pinzon bangs down his fist and says: ·

'Then, if you will not render the King's account, by the Rood, you shall render mine! You have your debt to me, Señor Columbus. To me, too, you promised these fine things, and I have done all my share to earn them, have I not? Yet our treasure is almost at hand's reach, and you will not turn aside to pick it up. I could lead you to it in a day! Repay your debt, señor!'

And so it went on between them, Pinzon raging, the Admiral quiet and dry at first, and then louder and very stiff, for some ten minutes. Then the Admiral became very silent, until suddenly he cried out:

'Martin, Martin, peace on this silly quarrel. Have we no better sense than to wrangle like children? Go back to your ship, and we will talk again to-morrow, when our heads are cooler. Forgive me if I have wronged you, and let us forget this!'

Martin Alonzo stamped out of the cabin and returned to the *Pinta* without saying another word.

The fleet became separated as the day drew on, owing to the contrary wind. Towards evening, it was blowing hard, with a rough sea, and as we were near a good anchorage the Admiral decided to put into shelter for the night, so as not to lose one another in the darkness. The light was already fading. We signalled the other ships to put back, and the *Niña* replied, and came about. Not so the *Pinta*. She appeared not to have noticed our signal and to be holding her course, a long way to the east. The Admiral had us signal twice again, but still she did not come about, and we hoisted a lamp to the masthead to mark our position. We could see her poop-lanterns far out in the darkness, growing smaller and dimmer, until presently they had faded out of sight. It was supposed at first that she had put in further down the coast, but when morning came there was not a sign of her to be seen. The *Pinta* had gone.

Martine Alonzo had deserted, and gone his own ways. What became of him I do not know. We who remain on Hispaniola have never seen him since. Perhaps in Spain, if both reached home in safety, the Admiral will find him again. But this story, like the *Niña* and the *Santa Maria*, must pursue its course without him.

He was a fine sailor, and men admired him almost without

exception. Yet there were few who would take his part against the Admiral. The crew who, a few weeks previously, had been openly in mutiny, were now the first to blame Pinzon for his desertion. In the end, it was the Admiral who was proved the stronger man.

CHAPTER EIGHTEEN

Hispaniola

SEEMINGLY, the Admiral had meant to stay out the winter in the Indies, and to return home in the Spring. But with the desertion of the *Pinta* he changed his plans. For another two weeks we sailed eastwards along the coast of Cuba, still vainly hoping to see something of the *Pinta*, until we arrived at the extreme point of land. Here the country sheers away westwards towards India, and here the Admiral took his decision to sail no more in that direction, but to return home, exploring only such likely lands as lay in his path. Perhaps he was influenced by the thought that Martin Alonzo might reach home before him, and claim the glory of the discovery. At least this was possible. We turned our backs on the west, and so discovered the country which has promised, and may yet fulfil, the best of all – the beautiful island of Hispaniola.

The Indians call it Bohio. From that easternmost point of Cuba where we lay on the 5th of December, we could see its rugged peaks above the horizon, very clear and blue in the tropic sky. But they warned us against approaching so dangerous a place. They said it was inhabited by savages called Caribs and Canibales, who were eaters of men, who had dogs' heads or, sometimes, single eyes in the middle of their foreheads. Nevertheless, we sailed. If there is any truth in these Indian tales we are likely soon to find out; but until so short a while ago we had seen none but the most kind and handsome of people, living a life so virtuous and carefree that we men of Europe, alas, might well envy them.

As we drew near, the island looked a Paradise on Earth. Lofty mountains climbed up into the clouds that crowned them, and looked down upon the green luxury of wood and valley which skirted them about. Waterfalls sprayed down their sides, and on among ferns and grottoes to the rivers, and the rivers to a sea so clear that a ship would seem to be sailing in the air, above the coral forests where fish, like streams of coloured light blown in the wind, wove in and out. Where we dropped anchor, we could see it going down ten fathoms in a froth of bubbles.

All along the coast were fields under cultivation. From the trees, columns of smoke rose up. By night the little fires twinkled far and near. Here was a society more numerous and less savage than any we had yet seen in these regions.

We touched the coast at several places, but the inhabitants fled before us. Then we anchored in a beautiful harbour which the

Admiral named Port Concepcion, and a party of us landing there, found a young woman, whom they brought aboard to the Admiral. She was too terrified even to struggle. In the usual way, the Admiral loaded her with ornaments and clothing (which she needed) and set her ashore to give an account of us to her people. The results were magical. Some two hours later a vast throng came down to the beach, in their midst being a person on a litter. It was their chieftain, the cacique. He entered his canoe and came out to us, his attendants in canoes also, and a swarm of people swimming. His bearing was majestic, and his dress magnificent. From his ears and around his neck, upon his wrists, his fingers and his ankles, were strings of seashells and ornaments of gold. On his head was a plumed headdress and both his tunic and his cloak were embroidered with feathers in a thousand colours.

He had brought gifts for the Admiral, among them a golden belt, beautifully wrought; and the Admiral bade him sit down and eat. A table had been set out on the upper deck under the canopy. The savage sat cross-legged upon a cushion which his attendants brought for him. He ate but little of the food that was set before him, tasted it only, out of courtesy, and had the rest sent down to his attendants, who, when the meal was over, brought water for him to wash his hands. A little later there came aboard an excited and voluble savage who turned out to be the husband of the young girl whom we had made our ambassadress. He was delighted with the gifts, and made a very long and animated speech to express his thanks, kissing the deck many times before the Admiral's feet. As Coatta explained afterwards:

'He say much thank, most happy, Great Lord. Wife, too, much thank, most happy. Wife make pretty view. All village rejoice. Heaven give Great Lord much family.'

The village lay inland about a mile from the sea, and a road led up to it between well-cultivated fields. It must have contained a thousand houses, big and small, and there was a great square before the house of the cacique, which stood in its own garden. In this square, a few nights later, a feast was held, which lasted until dawn. We were royally entertained. The principal food was fish, which they stuff with spices and cook upon spits over the fire. Every kind of fruit was brought to us; and there is a root vegetable called *potato* which, when cooked, has a very delicate and pleasing flavour. This, with maize, is one of their chief foods.

A strange custom of these natives is that of breathing smoke. We have observed it everywhere in the Indies, but I cannot remember that any traveller from the East has told of it. There is a plant which the Indians call *tobacco*. When the leaves of it are dried, they will kindle and smoulder, giving off a great quantity of intoxicating smoke. The Indians roll the leaf and kindle it at one end, breathing in the smoke through the other, and puffing it out through their mouths and noses in an extraordinary manner. Or sometimes they have a forked stick, hollowed and tipped at the single end with clay. The forked end they put into their two nostrils, and holding the other over the smouldering leaves, thus breathe in the smoke through the nose. It was one of these Smoking Pipes that we had picked up at sea, shortly before we first sighted land. I myself once tried smoking this tobacco, but it set me coughing so much I have not attempted it since. Others it made sick. Yet those few of us who have persisted in it say that with custom it has a most soothing effect. Still I cannot think it a fit practice for a Christian.

The young cacique was a local chieftain only. He told us that the Great Cacique of the country, whose name is Guacanagari, had learned of our coming, and was already on his way to greet us. His own town was situated at a three days' journey along the coast.

When he came it was with a noble following. As he approached we could hear the drums and singing beyond the fields of maize. He was carried in a litter on the shoulders of eight men, and surrounded by his counsellors. Behind walked his sons and their wives, and a retinue of caciques and people with gifts. Before him went the drummers and dancers, and a number of women with long canes, on which were perched singing birds, tied by the leg.

There was another feast that night. The Admiral sat next to Guacanagari, who treated him with great honour, and afterwards presented him with the gifts he had brought. There was some quantity of gold, both nuggets and dust. He told the Admiral that there was much of it to be found on the island, but mostly inland, among the mountains, where his people dared not go for fear of the warlike Caribs, who were, it seemed, the real masters of the island. It is a region called by the Indians, Zibao, which we believe to be the same as Zipango.

There can be few people upon earth so peaceful by nature as these Indians of the coast. They have few laws and keep them all; few belongings with which they do not willingly part. Most things they own in common, and what work is to be done they do for the common good. Heathen and uncivilized they may be, but they have shown us Christian treatment. Would God we had returned as much!

We delayed in this pleasant place until the 24th of December, Christmas Eve. Guacanagari had returned to his own village. We had spent idle days with little else to be done but take food and water aboard the ships. Then we sailed. Little did we know that it was to be the last sailing of the *Santa Maria*.

Mendoza

CHAPTER NINETEEN

Christmas Eve

IT WAS SO warm that evening off Hispaniola! It was hardly possible to think that this was Christmastide when the cold winds blow down to Palos from the snowy plains of Castile! There was hardly a breath of wind. The sea was glassy. All was so still after the sun went down that you fancied you heard the nightingales singing over on the island. Men talked quietly in the darkness until they began to yawn, and one by one, wrapped themselves in their cloaks and lay down to sleep. Only I, and the helmsman, remained awake.

I leaned on the bulwarks, listening to the gentle lapping of the water, watching the moonlight twinkling in the wake of the little *Niña*, half a mile to seaward. How peaceful it all was! From afar came the faint regular sound of the waves breaking on the beach, lulling me to sleep. I began to count them, drowsily, breaking, breaking, breaking. The wind must lie off the shore to-night, I said to myself, or we should not hear them so well from here.

Then I thought: But the wind is not in that quarter! And I listened again. It seemed to me that the waves could be heard more clearly now – too clearly. I looked across to the shore, and it was nearer than it had been a while ago.

'It should be Mendoza at the helm, and he knows his job,' I said to myself. I walked over to the tiller. There I found not Mendoza, but Pepe.

'What are you doing here?' I said. 'Do you want to wreck us? Where's Mendoza?'

'He's not well,' replied the boy. 'He went below to get some sleep. I'm all right, I can sail the ship.'

'The devil you can! Listen to those breakers! There's a strong current running, and we'll be on top of 'em if you don't watch out. Put your tiller over . . . Careful now! And hold it there till I come back.'

So Mendoza was asleep below, leaving a boy to manage the ship! Maybe I should have taken charge myself. Instead I hurried angrily to the forecastle to fetch Mendoza to his post. I had hardly set my foot on the ladder, when there came a hollow rumbling sound, and the ship gave a stagger that threw me forward on my head. Another great lurch, the deck sloping, the awakened crew stampeding for the hatchway. I lay on the boards, almost unconscious, with the men stepping over me. José Murela raised me up.

'You all right, Miguel? Quick, we've run aground! God knows how. . . .'

Alone in the forecastle, I supported myself a moment against the side. A trickle of water was coming in through the seams. I bathed my forehead, and went on deck.

There was pandemonium. They had cut loose the sails, and several of them had crowded into the boat. The Admiral ordered them to row the anchor out to deep water, so that we could warp her off. Instead, they rowed for all they were worth towards the *Niña*. We shouted after them, but they only rowed the faster. When they got there, Vincent Pinzon turned them back. Roldan appeared, and shouted across to the Admiral:

'Her seams are opening, señor! The water's coming in fast! Shall we bring the cargo on deck?'

'Yes!' cried the Admiral. He buried his face in his hands for a moment, and murmured, 'God! Help me to save her!' I was standing just near him. He looked up and said: 'Miguel, get out the axes from the chest. Quickly, man! We must cut away the masts to lighten her! It's our only chance!'

Every man that could get an axe, hewed till the sweat poured off him. The masts fell one by one into the sea and we severed the rigging. By then our boat had returned, with another from the *Niña*. The anchor was carried out and for an hour we sweated at the capstan. It was too late. She was fast on the reef, and we could not move her an inch.

With step heavy as lead, the Admiral mounted the stairs to the quarter deck, walked wearily to his cabin, entered, shut the door behind him.

The *Santa Maria* was a total loss, in a calm sea, beneath a cloudless sky.

* * * *

There was nothing to be done till daylight. We sat around dejectedly, hardly even talking. Somebody went about putting out all the lanterns, one by one, for no reason I suppose, but for something to do. Vincent Pinzon came aboard, and went in to the Admiral.

A little later we heard a sound of sobbing. It was Pepe. He was huddled against the stump of the mainmast, crying his heart out. In all the turmoil he had been quite forgotten, and now that it was over nobody cared about him enough even to curse him. Only Sancho looked round.

'And after all I taught him, too,' he muttered presently, and spat. Nothing else was said.

CHAPTER TWENTY

Farewell to the Admiral

FISHERMEN, COMING out with the first light of morning, saw the wreck, and took the news to Guacanagari. We had been cast away almost within a bowshot of his village. In great haste he rose up, called his servants together, and the whole company rowed out to us.

When he saw the tangled wreckage that had once been the *Santa Maria* he made a great lamentation, and it was with the tears streaming down his face that he came before the Admiral. Never could we have expected to find, in an untutored savage, so much compassion, or Christian charity. He summoned all his people and all his canoes, and bade them help us to salvage our goods. All our stores, gear, cargo, everything that could be moved, was taken ashore and carried into the village. He appointed a guard to watch over it, and set others to work to build huts to store it all until further need. We lacked for nothing. Within two days, the wreck had been dismantled, and we were housed and cared for in everything. For the Admiral and his lieutenants there was service and hospitality in Guacanagari's own house. For the crew, there was the hospitality of the whole village.

We lay stretched at ease under the palms, and flung stones into the sea. But a time came when we began to review our situation.

'We are nicely trimmed now,' said José, 'but what of the return? There lies the *Niña*. Not much over fifty feet of her. Room aboard for a crew of, say, twenty-five. How can she carry the fifty-odd from the *Santa Maria*, with their provisions and all, to say nothing of the Indians and merchandise we have picked up here, and hope to see Spain again? She would sink before she had gone a league.'

'Some will have to stay,' said I.

'And why not?' said Mosca. 'Who would want to go back? I know when I am well off.'

'I am no longer young. I don't wish to see my last days out among the heathen,' said José. 'I have a married daughter in Palos town, and a little grandson. He is to be a priest when he grows up, his mother says, and I would like to see him again before they shave off his locks.'

'I have holes in my shoes,' said Mosca, 'and the roads are hard in Spain. I have a ragged cloak, and the Spanish winter is cold. I will stay here even if I stay alone.'

He soon found that there were many who felt as he did, I being among them. After some consultation among ourselves, we went to the Admiral and put our case before him. It would be hopeless for so many to try to reach home in so small a ship. Let us remain behind, and hold the island for him until his return. The Admiral smiled as he had not done since Christmas Day.

'It will be no hardship, eh, lads?'

'No, señor, it will be no hardship.'

'First come, first served,' said the Admiral. 'As you say, I could not take you all, and you may stay if you wish to. But make no mistake about it. Remember – I may not return.'

He let his words sink in.

'It is a long voyage. You know how long. You know the dangers. And the *Niña* is – well, good fortune be with her, but I have seen stouter vessels.'

We said we would take that chance.

'So be it, then,' he replied. 'And now I will tell you this: Three days ago, when we went aground, I thought God had turned His face from me, for my sins; that He had found me unworthy of the success with which, so far, I had been blessed. I should have had more faith than to think so. I now believe it is God's will for us to found a colony here, for the glory of Spain and the Christian Faith. Were we not wrecked upon Christmas Day, of all days in the year, and at midnight, the very hour of the Nativity? It is a blessing, not a curse, that has been given to us. Moreover, I find that there are great riches on this island, and the cacique has promised to bring us as much gold as we need. We shall do a good trade here. It is for us to build a fort, and hoist the flag of Spain.'

'What need of a fort, Señor Admiral, where people live in peace?'

'You are sailors. A sailor without a ship is a sailor without discipline. The fort shall be your ship, and Don Diego your Captain. You see,' he went on, 'I have already laid my plans, and am ready for work. I have found a good site for building. The *Santa Maria* will provide us with stout timber, cannon and ammunition, ready to hand. The Indians will give their labour, and in a fortnight, with God's blessing, the work should be finished.'

Except for details, it was finished in ten days. The place lies about a mile from the village on the other bank of the river, where is a little hill looking out to sea. On the inland side are the woods, from which we got much timber. We built the fort with store-rooms, armoury and dwelling quarters, thatched it over with palm branches, and surrounded it with a stockade, mounting our guns at the four corners. This is the Fort of La Navidad – The Nativity – so named in commemoration of the day when we were wrecked. This was the home of thirty-eight men who remained behind on Hispaniola. This is the outpost whose eight surviving defenders keep guard day and night against the Indian arrows. This is the place where now I write these lines.

As I told you, the Admiral put Don Diego de Araña in command. Under him were Pedro Guttierez and a certain Rodrigo de Escobedo, a young Castilian of good family, who had sailed in the *Niña*. Also, there remained with us Mosca, Mendoza, Juan Lopez. Old José Murela went home to his daughter and grandson, and one-eared Rodrigo de Triana to his ten thousand maravedis, the reward promised to the first to sight land. But Sancho Gil stayed; and Pepe. The crew of the *Niña* refused to take him aboard, declaring he would bring them bad luck, so the lad has lived out his penance at La Navidad.

The Admiral went on board on the night of the 2nd of January. Before he went he held a great meeting in the open before the fort, at which were assembled the whole company of Spaniards, together with a multitude of Indians, and Guacanagari, in state, attended by the caciques of all the regions round about.

'O Guacanagari,' said the Admiral, 'these men I leave with you, to be your neighbours. Friendship they will repay with

friendship, love with love. They will teach you the ways of white men, and of the Christ, their God. They will protect you from your enemies. They will trade with you for your gold and spices, and deal justly with you. They will be as your brothers; may you be also as a brother to them. And in six months I will return to you again.'

The Indian pledged his friendship and placed a collar of gold around the Admiral's neck, receiving in return, a scarlet cloak. Then, to us, the Admiral said:

'You have heard my words to the Cacique. Let them be binding to you also. When I return in June, or at the latest, July, I shall bring with me a fleet whose sails will span the horizon. Meanwhile, this little fort is to be your home, but where it stands, where you stand, is Christian soil, Spanish soil. Guard it well. Nourish well the friendship we have with these good Indians. Give your obedience to Don Diego, and everything shall prosper with you!'

He hoisted our Standard to the mast above the watch tower; we sang the *Salve Regina*, and then knelt in prayer for the safety of the *Niña*. Lastly, to impress the Indians with our strength, we let off one of the cannon. A skilful aim brought down a tree at fifty paces. The Indians were stricken with awe to see such magic.

One thing more. The statue of the Holy Virgin which had stood over his door on the flagship, the Admiral now gave to us. It remains still upon the eastern wall of the fort, where we placed it, looking towards Spain.

Long after dark, the last of the returning crew having gone aboard, the Admiral took farewell of Don Diego and entered his boat. It pushed off, and in a few moments had passed beyond the smoky torchlight. The sound of the oars died away.

Next day there was no wind, and they could not sail, but none came ashore. We did not see the Admiral again.

Then, on the morning of the 4th of January, the wind arose with the sun, and the *Niña* shook out her sails. She moved from her anchorage and, as she passed the gaunt skeleton of the *Santa Maria*, fired a salute. We answered it. The sound awoke the parrots from the trees, and noisy flocks of them flew up and away with the echoes of the cannon. But silent were we who watched the little *Niña* heading seaward, tinier still, more distant, with every minute that passed.

Farewell, Don Christopher Columbus! Farewell, little *Niña*! God speed you safe to harbour!

Don
Diego

CHAPTER TWENTY-ONE

Don Diego

THAT WAS seven months ago. Seven long months. June and
July have passed without any sign of the Admiral.

Before he sailed he had drawn up a code of regulations for the
fort. The gate was to be opened at sunrise, closed at sunset, when
all men were to be present to answer the roll call. None were to
venture far without leave from the Commander; none were,
under any circumstances, to go beyond the boundary of Guacanagari's country. Our business was to trade with the Indians,
collecting as much gold, silver and spices as we could by the time
of his return. For some time the fort was the centre of activity
in our part of the island and was thronged all day with bartering
Indians. Don Diego kept account of every tittle. A shrewd,
good-humoured little man, always dressed in neat black clothes

(still neat, even now, though patched and faded), his careful government was not questioned during our first months, and might never have been but for two things. First of these was the fever.

About a quarter of a mile to the east of La Navidad, the forest conceals a swamp the extent of which we did not know until the fort was well under construction; and even when known we regarded it as a factor in our defence, not as a drawback. True, the site had been hurriedly chosen, but it stood on raised ground, and caught the breezes from the sea. No reason to suppose it unhealthy. But after a succession of hot, stagnant, broiling days, the slightest breeze would carry with it, not freshness, but the vapours and mosquitoes of the marsh, infecting everything with a pestilence. This we did not discover until the hot days of March.

Before then, Don Diego had had some trouble to keep all the men in the fort. Among the hospitable Indians there was leisure and lodging to be found. Some of us began to stay away from La Navidad without returning for two or three nights. The easy life of Hispaniola drugged away all warnings of possible danger (not that this was ever much contemplated), and with every passing day there would be another name unanswered at the roll call. So, when certain men had not been seen for ten days at a stretch, Don Diego sent out search parties, who found them living like princes in a village several miles away. They were brought back under arrest, to be chained up in the guard-room for another ten days. "And that is leniency!' said Don Diego.

Under other circumstances such measures would have been effective. But these were the hot days of March I spoke of. La Navidad was like a furnace. In the baking heat, one of the prisoners, a man named Tomás, sat and shivered with cold, and in the cold night he burned with heat. Next morning he was dead.

We buried him. At high noon, Gonzago Podrilla was taken with vomiting. Two other men fell ill before sunset, and one of them we buried next day. The fever spread rapidly. Gonzago died and there was a scare that we had the plague. Then Don Diego himself was stricken, and Guttierez and Escobedo had to maintain what discipline they could between them. There was little they could do, however, since nearly everyone had already fled to the

healthier climate of the Indian villages. They themselves soon followed.

But the wind changed, blowing freshly off the sea, and the fever left us. This was the worst bout we have had, and cost us four of our men. For Don Diego, when he was on his feet again, the problem was how to get the absentees back to the fort. At this time his authority was still felt strongly enough to succeed part of the way. With difficulty, two-thirds were persuaded to return. The others managed somehow to remain among the Indians, and have done much there to degrade the name of Spaniard. Mendoza was one of the first of them. He grew fat and oily as a slug, lay all day in his hammock, and had an Indian boy to fan him and keep away the flies. To my surprise, Mosca left us. Where he went I do not know. We did not see him again for four months.

The second thing that helped to shipwreck the government of La Navidad, was the character of Rodrigo de Escobedo. This swaggering young blade had a second name, which was Greed, and a third which was Ambition. He was out to make his fortune, and was soon chafing under the sober command of Don Diego; in this he found an ally in Pedro Guttierez. Escobedo was handsome and well spoken, knew how to make himself popular, and had a fund of clever-sounding advice upon all occasions – advice which was taken too often.

But this is to anticipate. For a time it seemed that things were coming to rights, and we had laid in supplies of medicines that the Indians use against fever, so that when it returned, as it sometimes did, we should be better prepared.

But alas, against the fever of Gold, the Indians had no remedy, and to this, every one of us succumbed in some degree. 'Find me gold,' the Admiral had said. It was the one injunction which was undertaken all the time with a whole heart, and at first, it looked as though it would be an easy matter. The Indians seemed to have little value for it. I have seen one of them exchange a good handful for a single hawk's bell, and even then the knavish Spaniard swore at him for a cheat because he left a few grains sticking to the moisture of his hand. There seemed no extreme to which Spanish cupidity would not go; the more gold was found, the more was demanded. Guacanagari, still friendly, sent out to collect it for us in every region of his domain, and it began to look as though the Admiral would return to a full treasury, notwithstanding the fact that the men were keeping good pickings of their own.

When the stream of gold started to run dry, the real trouble began. The Indians explained that there was no more to be found. Needless to say they were not believed, and, since they could not be coaxed, the old fable arose that they were holding out for a better bargain. The Spaniards began to use other methods.

I will not describe the degrees by which La Navidad became little better than an encampment of brigands. Don Diego could do nothing to stop the decay once it had set in, and the best he could hope for was the early return of the Admiral. He was the only one with foresight enough to fear a rising of these Indians who had once been our friends and helpers, and whom we were now teaching, first to suspect, then to fear, and at last, to hate us. Behind it all was Escobedo, with Sancho and Juan Lopez at his right hand.

One day Don Diego sent for Guacanagari, to talk with him. The Cacique did not come. Swallowing his pride, Don Diego himself went to the Cacique's house, only to be told that he was ill, that he had gone away. Returning through the forest, he met a small company of Indians, who stood aside for him to pass, and as he approached he saw that they were carrying something – the body of an Indian boy, dead, striped across and across with the red stripes of a whip. The Indians said no word, only turned their heads away and shuffled slowly past him towards their village.

'By the Cross!' cried Don Diego, 'I will hang that Escobedo high as Haman!'

Yet who could make a noose for Escobedo's neck? Not Don Diego. There was now scarce a man to back him against his lieutenant, as well he knew. Escobedo made the noose himself.

*　　　*　　　*　　　*

Beyond the farthest borders of Guacanagari's domain, lies the mountainous country of Zibao. In Zibao are the mines which provide all the riches of the island; but in Zibao also dwell the fierce tribes of the Caribs and Canibales, under their warrior king, Caonabo. To these people fighting and bloodshed are the two staples of life, and they are said to feed on human flesh. Yet, despite this, it had sometimes been suggested that we should send an expedition to explore this country for the gold mines, though Don Diego had always refused to sanction it, our numbers being too small and it being against the express commands of the Admiral. Now, however, Escobedo and his followers were in no mood for such restraints. A few Spaniards and a whip could bring a whole continent of Indians to their knees, and where the whip failed, the sword and musket would succeed. Moreover, these tales of the man-eating King Caonabo were not given much credence. Escobedo and Guttierez planned their expedition, and were determined to lead it into Zibao, with or without the consent of Don Diego.

And it must be said that they had one shrewd reason for their determination. Supposing that the Admiral returned within his appointed time, which was now not more than a month ahead, they had short shrift to look for. Not only were they guilty of mutiny, cruelty and theft, but for all their bullying they had wrung from the wretched Indians far less than Don Diego had obtained by better means. Unless they could show a more fortunate account than this they were faced with imprisonment and disgrace, if not the gallows. Their only hope lay in discovering the fabulous gold mines of Zibao. Enough money makes a lenient judge!

So they assembled twenty men, Sancho and Juan Lopez among them, and a party of Indian guides and carriers. When all were ready, Escobedo came in with a swagger to Don Diego, to demand the keys of the armoury and storehouse.

'And what if I refuse to give them to you?' asked the Commander.

'By St. Jago's blood, we will break down the door!' was the reply.

Don Diego took the keys and walked to the door. Then he suddenly turned and flung them far over the stockade into the river.

'Do so,' he said grimly. 'And remember it when Don Christopher returns!'

Escobedo cursed, and turned on his heel. They broke open the armoury and took all they needed, shared out provisions to last a month, and were prepared to march. Then it was discovered that Sancho was missing. They delayed a whole day waiting for him, but he did not reappear. 'Let him rot where he is, then,' said Escobedo, and they went without him.

There remained only four Spaniards to hold La Navidad: Don Diego, Hernan, Pepe and myself. The others who had not gone with the expedition were living their own lives, Heaven knows where, among the Indians. The fort was like a place of the dead. Nevertheless, with this small garrison Don Diego kept the flag flying, closed the gates at sunset, and kept constant look-out for the Admiral's sail.

CHAPTER TWENTY-TWO

Waiting

ON THE second day following the departure of Guttierez and Escobedo, I saw a canoe coming down the river. The two occupants drew it on to the bank, unloaded their bundles and started up the hill towards the fort. I was curious about it, for it was a long time since the Indians had come willingly to trade at La Navidad. Then, as the first drew near, I recognized him. It was Mosca.

He had grown his hair long, Indian fashion, which, with his beard, made him look as wild a man as any under the sky. His dress was a loincloth and a pair of sandals. In his belt was a knife and a sheaf of arrows; in his hand a bow, and in his mouth, a smoking roll of tobacco. Behind him walked an Indian woman with the bundles.

'A good day to you, Miguel,' says Mosca. 'Have you room for a renegade in the fort?'

'We've room enough and to spare,' said I, 'but you'll have to speak with the commander.'

They came in. The woman sat down with her bundles in the shade. Presently Don Diego appeared on the scene.

'All or nothing,' said Mosca, puffing at his tobacco. 'You'll have to take us as we are, señor. The woman is a good shot with a bow. What's more, she can cook.'

'Why should I need either of you?' asked Don Diego.

'From now on you're going to need everyone you can get,' replied Mosca. 'There's trouble coming, and I hope you've kept your powder dry.'

'I have,' said Don Diego, tartly.

Mosca took another puff at his tobacco, and said: 'Escobedo left here yesterday morning, didn't he? There were nineteen of them, making towards the Zibao Mountains.'

'Did you know? Where did you see them?'

'I didn't see them. But news travels fast among the Indians; though not in your direction I fancy. Did you know that Sancho is dead?'

The question was put so suddenly, and in such an ominous tone, that none voiced the query that sprang immediately to our minds. We waited for Mosca to explain.

'Oh, yes,' he went on, 'Sancho's dead all right. And I have seen his body. It is hanging head downwards over the ashes of a fire. The place is not ten miles from here.'

I remembered what Escobedo had said when Sancho was missed: 'Let him rot where he is then!' And I shuddered inwardly.

'It served him right,' said Mosca. 'The fool! The Indians called him the Red Grindstone. Well, he has ground his last red ounce. Lucky it was for Señor Escobedo that he had not the habit of walking in the forest alone!'

'Escobedo must be recalled to the fort!' says Don Diego on the instant.

'Impossible, señor! You'll say it's not my place to give advice, but here it is just the same: let Escobedo look to himself. You haven't a single man to spare to send after him, and if you had, do you think he'd listen? No, señor, your best chance is to warn the others in the village. Get them back to the fort while there is still tir e.'

'How much time have we?'

'That's what I don't know; but enough time for that, if we're quick. And then we must hold out until the Admiral returns – if we can.'

'If we can?' echoed Don Diego. 'But with a few more men we shall be safe enough. Guacanagari will not attack the fort.'

'Señor, he has sent to the Caribs for help. The war drums are sounding in the mountains. If Caonabo comes, we shall need look to our muskets. He will attack. Dolores warned me of all this, and I have lost no time coming here to tell you.'

'Dolores . . . ?'

Mosca pointed to the Indian woman, sitting patiently among her bundles.

'She,' he said, 'is Dolores. Well, señor, do we stay or do we go?'

'You stay,' said Don Diego.

❋   ❋   ❋   ❋

I found Mendoza in his hut. At first he would not take the warning seriously and declared there was no change in the Indians, that I was joking. Then he allowed himself to be persuaded to the point of saying he would come back in the next few days. 'I know the Indians,' he said. 'There's no danger for the moment. I have a few things to pack up, then I'll come.'

Elsewhere I was greeted with the same response. Yes, they would come – in a few days. The days went by, and only three had returned: Luiz de Torres, Lucas, and Herries, the Irishman. The others stayed until to-morrow, and on the morrow forgot, or put it off again. We warned them a second time and still they did not come. Thereafter, we felt it was becoming too great a risk to send any of our small number again to the village.

So there were eight of us, and the Indian woman Dolores who refused to be sent away. She waited on Mosca, followed him everywhere, and took orders from no one else. He set her to cook and sew for us and taught her how to clean and load the muskets. When I took the fever – and it was a bad spell which kept me more than a week in my hammock – it was she who nursed me. Meanwhile, we worked to put our defences in order, and cleared back the bushes and scrub as far as we could, so as to afford no cover for the enemy. Sometimes a few Indians would come to watch us, some even came to trade. But that stopped after a while, and we were left strangely alone to count the long tedious days. There was no news of Caonabo or his warriors. We began to grow restless, to ask ourselves if the danger was not imaginary after all; but the answer lay in the very stillness. Then one day, we saw five great war canoes go past along the coast, some distance out to sea. We did not see where they put in, and they made no sign as they went by. It was about this time, while I was still weak from the fever, that I began writing this account. It helped to quieten the anxieties that were pressing on my mind.

One night, while we were talking around the fire, Hernan suddenly sat bolt upright, and said, 'Hush!' Talk stopped, and we listened.

Very distant – the noise of drums!

None slept all that night, but the attack did not come. Then, with daylight, when we were thinking of turning in for rest, we heard a shout from the forest beyond the river. A single figure ran out from the trees, a fat figure, running heavily, shouting and waving to us. It was Mendoza. He stumbled and fell, and there was an arrow jutting in his back.

'The Indians!' cried Mosca. 'At last! To arms!'

They were keeping among the trees. As Mendoza scrambled to his feet, they let fly a shower of arrows which lanced into the ground on every side of him. He was struck again, in the leg and in the shoulder. He stumbled and limped on down to the river, plunged in and started to swim, arrows still splashing around him. We fired into the trees and the Indians drew back for a moment, but Mendoza had stopped swimming, half-way across. He struggled feebly and there was a red stain on the water. Lucas cried out he would fetch him in and ran to the gate. Don Diego shouted to him to come back, but he was already on the river bank, where, next moment, an arrow got him in the foot. There was no time to reload our muskets and the Indians were coming from the wood again, swarms of them. Quick as thought, Don Diego turned the cannon on them, fired, and once again they fled. To make sure, we let off the second cannon. Mosca ran out and dragged Lucas into the fort. He had crawled back a little of the way, and there fainted. Meanwhile, Mendoza lay like a log, drifting past the fort down river. Presently he sank to the bottom.

Lucas was in great pain. 'Poison,' muttered Don Diego, when he looked at the wound. The Indian woman came forward without a word, sucked away the poison as well as she could, dressed the wound with little leaves, and bound it up. Presently Lucas said it felt easier. But he has not yet recovered. His whole leg is useless. The woman constantly changes the dressing and cleans the wound, but he still complains, sometimes, of the pain.

That was the beginning. The Indians did not reappear for another two days, and then came in force, attacking us from all sides. I do not know how we managed to beat them off. They returned again and again to the attack, and every time we repulsed them with arrows and musket shot. (The guns we use only as a last resort, so as to keep fresh their effect.) We killed fifteen of them. After dark they crept out and dragged the bodies away.

Then more waiting and more waiting. Sometimes it looked as though the Indians had forgotten us altogether, or we would see only a few of them watching from the trees. There would be days of awful stillness, followed by days and nights when the drums beat unceasingly, coming from every direction, far and near. Then quietness again.

So it goes on. It is safest to sleep by day when it is easy for only a couple of men to keep a sharp watch. By night, if there is no moon, we have torches burning all along the stockade, throwing just enough light to prevent us being taken completely by surprise, but it needs every pair of eyes on the look-out, and weapons ready in our hands. For the rest, we have sufficient food, though to get water we must go down to the river whenever it is safe enough, so as to save what we have in the butts – which is, however, already none too sweet.

Escobedo has not returned. We hoped against hope that he might fight his way back, but have at last resigned ourselves to it that we shall see none of them again. By our reckoning, it is now mid-August, however, and any day may bring the Admiral's ships on the horizon. Until that day comes we have little to do but keep watch, keep courage, and keep our faith that he will, indeed, return. Pray God it may be soon!

※   ※   ※   ※

28th of August.

Without Fortune's help, we should have been overwhelmed this very day. The Indians attacked us with burning arrows, hoping to set light to the fort. The thatch would have blazed like tinder had

166

their aim been better. By a miracle only three arrows struck there, and every time we were able to drag away the fire before it spread. Then it came on to rain in torrents, the water is still streaming over everything, and we are saved again for the while. But our salvation is not unmixed with sadness, for we now know beyond all doubt the fate of the expedition to Zibao. In the van of the attacking savages we saw the head of Pedro Guttierez, carried on a pole; some of the Indians were armed with Spanish swords, others with Spanish shields. It is too horrible to think of.

* * * *

1st of September.

Poor Lucas has died, in spite of all our efforts. The poison slowly took possession of him and burned him away. All his last days he was barely conscious. We buried him this evening by the east wall of the fort, under the statue of the Holy Virgin. Don Diego read the prayers for him, bareheaded in the rain.

* * * *

4th of September.

It is still pouring with rain. It has barely ceased once since it began, and we have had squalls of high wind, thunder and lightning. Our great care is for the cannon and powder, which so far we have managed to keep dry. Everything is a swamp. The river is rising and La Navidad stands like an island on its hill. The streaming weather has brought our spirits low, and we cannot keep at bay the awful thought we have never dared before to think of, that the *Niña* never came to port, and that Don Christopher Columbus and all his crew have lain these last long months at the bottom of the ocean.

Don Diego has plans to abandon the fort. The *Santa Maria's* boat is in good repair, and big enough to carry us all, with just sufficient stores for a short voyage in fair weather. We have made a sail, and with a good wind, when the rains leave off, we may be able to slip away and outstrip the Indian canoes. We shall need a dark night and the favour of God. If these are granted to us we should be able to make the coast of Cuba, or some island where we can begin life anew.

Mosca has used up his store of tobacco and is very miserable for lack of it. Instead of smoking, he sits all day playing the dice with Pepe and Dolores.

Pepe is no longer a boy. His chin shows the beginnings of a black beard. He has grown tall and strong, and has stood his ground along with the rest of us without complaint. He brought down two Indians with his bow in the last skirmish.

It is very cold. If only the rain would cease!

Part Four :
Supper at La Rabida

CHAPTER TWENTY-THREE

The Guests

IT WAS in the year 1528 that Brother Antonio sat down in the library of La Rabida to write his account of Christopher Columbus; and as he dipped his pen he looked from the window across the harbour of Palos to the ocean Columbus had conquered, and he opened his writing with a description of the scene before him: 'The town and the harbour, the ships along the quay, and, out to the west, two galleons coming in from the far, rich countries of the New World.'

Brother Antonio bent to his writing; and the two galleons sailed over the bar of Saltes and dropped anchor in Palos harbour.

In the cabin of the larger vessel, a man sat working at his desk. He was a little over forty years of age, of middle height, well built, and dressed in clothes of a rich sobriety. His face was lean and sunburnt, and he stroked his thick dark beard with a hand on which gleamed one single ring of magnificent design.

There was a knock at the door. A young man entered.

'The anchor is down, General. How soon will you wish to go ashore?'

The man pushed back his chair.

'If I remember, Palos is a very small place,' he said, 'and has little to offer in the way of hospitality. I would probably do better to remain aboard. But let us go on deck, Gonzalo my friend, and see what is to be seen.'

They went out onto the poop. For some little time the General said nothing, but stood smelling the strong harbour-smell of fish and seaweed, and listening to the gulls, and gazing at the boats and the little town. Presently, he said:

'I have been reckoning, Gonzalo. It is twenty-six years since I last saw this, my native shore. Twenty-six years! And now, when you ask me how soon I want to set foot on it, I say maybe I'll stay on board ship! I must be growing old.'

Gonzalo laughed. 'Not old, General, but wise. It is a poor town.'

'Nay, but there you are wrong,' said the man. 'It is a very rich town, and one that will never be forgotten in Spain, I trust. Bethink you, my friend, it was from here that Christopher Columbus sailed. And that' – he counted on his fingers – 'that was thirty-six years ago.'

'Three years before I was born, General.'

'Truly? You do not look so young as that. Yet I could not have been more than eight myself, though I remember it very well. At least, I do remember him coming home again. What a triumph it was! And here have we dropped anchor in the same water, perhaps in the very same place as he dropped his! Well, if I were poetical by nature, I should make much of that; but instead, I am perplexed by wondering where I shall find lodging in this place. What,' he asked, pointing, 'is that big building over there on the hillside?'

Not knowing, Gonzalo called down to one of the boats from the town.

'That is a monastery, Excellency,' came the reply. 'The monastery of La Rabida.'

'La Rabida!' echoed the General. 'But of course! And that

174

is where I will stay. Gonzalo, have them send up to the good monks·
of La Rabida and say that Hernando Cortés requests their
hospitality for a few days.'

*　　　*　　　*　　　*

The Conqueror of Mexico went back to his cabin and sat for
a long time gazing out of the window. Evening had come on,
and the vesper bell was sounding from the church of St. George,
over in the town. He remembered how the bells had rung in
Medellin, in Seville, in Saragossa, all over Spain, when the great
Admiral came home! They did not ring now for Hernando Cortés.
He, Cortés, came unexpectedly to defend himself against the lies
and calumnies with which enemies were blackening his name at
Court. Well, he could refute them easily enough; and into the
bargain he had returned with such treasure as Columbus had never
laid eyes or hand on: two hundred thousand peso's worth of gold,
fifteen hundred marks of silver; spices, plants, rich stuffs and
pearls and emeralds from the vaults of the Lord Montezuma.

Montezuma! Closing his eyes, Cortés could see, as though in
life, the barbaric God-Emperor upon his throne in Chapultepec,
jewelled, and robed with feathers like some enormous and splendid
bird – and how neatly the Spaniards had trapped that bird!
One by one he had given up his treasure, his authority, his throne.
Less than four hundred strong, the Spaniards had hewed down
the Aztec Empire as though it were a tree.

They had burned their fleet behind them and turned inland,
marching from one battlefield to the next, two hundred miles of
mountain and jungle, to the gates of Mexico. Montezuma came
out to welcome them. The island city in the lake of Tezcuco,
with all its hundred temples, market-places, palaces, canals, and
floating gardens was laid open to the white invaders, and the

Emperor was a vassal in their hands. But only for a while. Montezuma had been slain by his angry people. From the summit of the temple of Huitzilopochtli, the Blood God, the war-horn sounded for deliverance. All through one terrible night, the Spaniards cut their way along the dark streets over the bodies of the dying, step by step across the beleaguered causeway to the mainland, from where next morning they watched the prisoners, their old comrades, hauled to the temple tops for sacrifice.

Cortés shuddered. A year later, he had taken his revenge upon the black priests, had thrown down the statues of Huitzilopochtli, Tlaloc and Tezcatlipoca from their sanctuaries, and there erected the Cross of Christ; but it was not enough to wipe out the memory of that savage ritual. The siege of Mexico had been hard and long, and the Aztecs were dying of hunger before they would bow their necks. Guatemotzin had fought like a panther to preserve his bloodthirsty and luxurious throne, but the Spaniards toppled it into the smoke of the ruined city and hanged him from a tree.

And now the conqueror had come back to Spain with an Empire in his pocket. Not all the jealous lies of his enemies would avail against that. He roused himself from his reflections, stretched, and looked around him. Already it was nearly dark. There came a knock at the door. It was Gonzalo, to say that the Conqueror would find a ready welcome at La Rabida.

※　　　　※　　　　※　　　　※

Cortés was accompanied to the monastery only by his secretary, one servant, and Gonzalo de Sandoval. They were met at the gate by an old monk who gave them a courteous and voluble welcome.

'I regret,' said the monk, 'that our Prior is not here himself to greet you. He is away in Saragossa, and has left me in charge

176

during his absence. I am Brother Antonio de la Vega. Your Excellency must please forgive my many shortcomings as a host. See, now, I am keeping you standing at the gate! If you will please to come with me—' He led the way, talking all the while with great animation, pointing out the features of the monastery as they went, explaining the arrangements he had made for his guests' convenience.

'We have prepared a room for you where you should not be too much disturbed. I hope you will be comfortable. Our life here is poor, but we are not altogether without the amenities. Over there, those windows, that is the refectory. But naturally, you can eat in private should you wish. I am having them prepare a meal for you now; a very simple meal, I'm afraid – yes, this way – but we have some quite good wine.'

He led down a stone corridor, past a door from which emerged the smell of cooking.

'In there, yes, are the kitchens. And that door at the end there is the guest room, where I have set for you. Oh—!' He stopped suddenly and turned. 'I am so sorry. I should have mentioned it earlier. There is another gentleman staying here, a kinsman of yours. . . .'

'Of mine?'

'So I understand. I have set for him at your table for to-night. I did not think you would object . . . ?'

'Indeed not! But who . . . ?'

'As I thought, as I thought. In any case, it is only for one night. He leaves to-morrow. But I should have told you earlier. Forgive me. Ah, here is the guest room."

They entered. From a chair by the window a man, short of stature and dressed entirely in black, with a pale face, small eyes, and a trim, curled beard, rose to his feet and advanced towards them. 'Don Hernando Cortés of Medellin?' he inquired.

Cortés bowed.

'My name is Francisco Pizarro. You would not remember me, perhaps.'

Cortés' puzzled frown left him, and his face lit up with a smile. He strode forward and gripped the other man warmly by the hand.

'Why, Francisco! Of course! No, I should not have recognized you. We have not met since we were boys.'

'When I used to keep pigs,' added Pizarro with a smile.

'I well remember the pigs,' laughed Cortés, 'and, in fact, I keep pigs myself now, on my estate in Cuba! I have heard,' he went on, when the laughter died down, 'that you, too, have been in the Indies?'

'Yes, for many years. I have been exploring southward from Panama, along the western coast. But that story will keep till later; I have no exploits to rival yours.'

Food was brought in, and the company sat down to table. Brother Antonio, as host, joined them and sat listening to the conversation. For the next hour there were tales of adventure, and discovery, strange races and stranger customs, Cuba, Mexico and the Pacific. Francisco Pizarro began to tell of his own discoveries. He told how he had followed a trail of rumours and legends, overcoming every kind of hardship, until he had reached the borders of a country far south of Mexico, where another Emperor held sway. 'His people call him the Inca, and his palace is said to be at a place called Cuzco, among the mountains. No white man has ever been there. I myself have not been beyond the borders of the country, but I have seen and heard enough to know how rich it is. The Inca is said to own treasure past all belief – though I myself can well believe it. The land abounds with gold.' Pizarro rubbed his hands together thoughtfully, and sipped his wine. He had come back to Spain, he said, to obtain

178

a Royal Warrant for himself as governor of the country which he was now returning to to explore.

Brother Antonio listened, glancing now and then at the face of the monk who had brought in and served the wine. It was a dark face, with a sharp, prominent nose and high cheekbones; not a Spanish face. The others had not noticed him, so absorbed were they in their talk. The meal was over, the chairs pushed back. The lamps were growing dim and the dark-faced monk moved quietly about the room to replenish them.

The company fell silent for a moment. Then Brother Antonio spoke, softly:

'Señores,' he said, 'as I have sat here listening to you. I have been thinking of other conversations I used to hear, years ago, in this very room where Christopher Columbus would sit talking with Father Juan Perez, our Prior in those days. You, Don Hernando, and you, Señor Pizarro, have inherited the fruit of those long talks they had, and to me, at least, it seems strange that you should have met in this, of all places.'

He stopped. Perhaps he should not have raised such ghosts, he thought; and immediately took up a lighter tone:

'But there! This is no time for such grave thoughts. Only it happens that I am writing my recollections of Columbus, and have him much in my mind at present.'

'You used to know him, then?' inquired Gonzalo.

'Why, yes, my son. You must remember it was from La Rabida that he sailed on his great voyage, and to La Rabida that he returned. He stayed here many times.'

The subject being opened, the old monk found he had an audience even more eager to listen to his recollections than to talk of their own. He began by telling how Columbus first came to the monastery, poor and unrecognized, leading his little son by the hand. Then he spoke of Father Juan Perez and Martin

179

Alonzo Pinzon, of Queen Isabella and how her friendship had given Columbus his opportunity at last. The story of the voyage he had heard from the lips of the Admiral himself, and from many another who had sailed with the Three Ships; and he himself had related it before more times than he could remember. But it could not be told too often. Once again he described the departure from Palos, the weeks of sailing, the failing hope, the mutinous crew, and, at last, the discovery of land.

'Is it true,' asked Gonzalo, 'that to the end of his days, he thought he had arrived in Asia?'

'Certainly. Although he made three other voyages to the New World, he died without knowing the truth of what he had discovered. But how should he have known better? Life is short. Had he been a younger man when fortune came to him he might have had time to correct his error.'

Brother Antonio went on, telling of the voyage among the islands, the desertion of Pinzon, the shipwreck and the building of La Navidad. Here he paused, and beckoned to the dark-faced monk, who all this while had been sitting in a far corner of the room.

'Brother Ignaçio, our guests will think poorly of us. Pray, fill their cups for them.'

Pizarro stroked his beard and watched the wine being poured.

'But Martin Alonzo rejoined the Admiral, did he not?' he asked.

Brother Antonio nodded.

'Two days after they sailed from La Navidad they met the *Pinta* again. I need not describe what joy and relief they felt.' He paused again and then said, 'But the story of the return voyage is not for me to tell. There is someone else in this room who should know it better.'

Eyebrows were raised in surprise.

'Brother Ignaçio sailed upon that voyage,' said the monk.

180

For the first time, the company looked up at the dark monk who, having set down the wine flask, was now standing by the old monk's chair. Recognition came immediately. 'An Indian!' thought Cortés, almost aloud.

'Yes,' said Brother Ignaçio, 'I am an Indian. My name, before I became baptized, was Coatta. Admiral Columbus brought me back with him after his first voyage.'

Brother Antonio urged him to tell the story. The monk sat down beside him, and for a short while said nothing, but gazed thoughtfully at his dark hands. The company waited in silence. Then he began.

CHAPTER TWENTY-FOUR

The Voyage Home

AS YOU have heard (said Coatta), two days after leaving Fort La Navidad, we met the *Pinta* again. We were making along the coast of Hispaniola, when the look-out man spied her sail in the distance. She came sweeping towards us, the wind full behind her, and all her canvas spread, and as she drew abreast we saw Martin Alonzo Pinzon on the poop, waving his cap. The Admiral signalled to him, and both ships put into a small harbour a little way back along the coast.

You will realize, of course, that I was then nothing but a naked savage, squatting with my fellows in a corner of the ship, an item of cargo being carried back to Spain to be – what shall I say? – to be exhibited to the King. It was unlikely that I should understand much of what happened there between Martin Alonzo and the Admiral. However, from what I saw myself and have since learned from others, it is not hard for me to piece together the facts.

When Martin Alonzo came aboard, the Admiral greeted him cordially. Whatever his thoughts may have been he kept them to himself. With the reappearance of the *Pinta* he had been spared a great danger. Not only would he have a companion ship upon the long voyage home, but the *Niña*, even allowing for the men we had left at the fort, was still gravely overloaded, and she could now share her burden with her sister ship. Moreover, the confidence of the sailors was greatly increased. This was certainly no time or place to rebuke Pinzon for his treachery.

Martin Alonzo, too, was anxious to be friendly. He smilingly explained that he had been parted from the Admiral by the bad weather, and had been trying all this while to locate and rejoin him. Desertion, he said, had never for a moment been in his mind. The Admiral accepted his excuses at their face value, but kept his suspicions. Martin Alonzo did not mention that he had been following the direction given by one of his Indians, thereby finding his way to a distant part of Hispaniola, where he had been trading on his own behalf; neither did he mention that he had obtained a great deal of gold, half of which he kept for himself and the other half divided among his crew to ensure their secrecy. The Admiral found all this out later. Meanwhile, amity was restored, if only in show, and the two ships sailed on together along the coast.

For a little while longer we remained among my native islands, the Admiral unwilling to leave where there was still so much to be explored. In particular he had heard reports of the island of Yamaye, and was half inclined, even now, to turn aside and seek it. But the sailors were growing impatient to see their families again, and at all costs he wished to avoid further trouble. He turned his ships to the sea and the homeland of my people at last faded away on the horizon. I have never seen it since.

I cannot remember how many Indians were with Martin Alonzo,

but we were seven on the *Niña*. Five of us were Aruacs, like myself, but the other two were Caribs whom the Admiral had taken aboard during our last days at Hispaniola. The Aruacs have always been a peaceful, friendly people, but the Caribs are our mortal enemies; for the first few days these two kept aloof from us, and we from them. Our hostility, however, soon vanished in a common fear. Imagine, if you can, what feelings were ours when the ships turned away to the open sea! Ignorant savages as we were, we had always believed the Great Water to be the edge of the world, peopled, if at all, by terrible ghosts and monsters. To venture into it was beyond all thinking. Somewhere on the other side, we thought, lived the immortal gods, those barbarous gods whose images, in the darkness of our idolatry, we worshipped. Indeed, when first we saw the Spanish ships, we truly believed that the gods had come back to us again. Yet here were we now sailing those fearful waters towards a destination we could not even begin to imagine. Under these circumstances the difference between a Carib and an Aruac was as nothing; we huddled together watching the grey water slip past us day after day, it seemed for ever.

It was very calm at first. We began to forget our fears, so much so that when there was no wind we used to dive into the sea and swim about between the ships. Sometimes birds alighted on the masts, and once a pelican flew on board. The sailors were all in good humour, their only anxiety being that the ships were very leaky, and that the *Pinta* was sailing badly. She had damaged her foremast, and could not carry much sail, and we had to stop many times for her to catch up with us.

The weather continued fair for nearly a month, though it was growing much colder. The sailors began to look for land, hoping they were near home, although the Admiral, I believe, knew that there was still far go to. Actually, at the time, we were in mid-ocean, somewhere near the islands known as the Azores. And here the storm came down on us.

The sea became rough. The wind blew violently from the north-east, growing stronger with every hour of the day and night. There was thunder and lightning. Next morning the gale was combing up the waves into ribbons of spray, and was so fierce that the sailors were forced to take in every inch of canvas. With bare masts we were beaten onwards from one wave to the next, the sea tossing and cresting high above us, splitting against our bows, drenching us, swamping us. The torn clouds scudded almost on top of us. Two miles away the *Pinta* was pitching and rolling with the sea breaking over her, sometimes lost among the waves, then tossed up higher than we, then veiled in the flying spray and sucked down again out of sight. 'God help her, she'll never last it out!' I heard one man shout, above the noise of the wind; and he began baling frantically as a huge wave burst against us and came foaming in. When evening came, the *Pinta* was yet farther off, labouring heavily. She had hoisted her lights to the masthead, so that we should not lose sight of her. We did the same. The lanterns swung back and forth overhead, and way out, the *Pinta's* glimmered, restlessly rocking, sometimes vanishing so long that we thought she had gone down; then, reappearing, always more and more distant. Oh! that terrible night! We Indians huddled together, drenched, hopeless, forgotten, sick. The waves towered up, hung over us, and came tumbling down with a roar louder even than the wind. The sailors never ceased their baling. Then the *Pinta's* lights vanished completely and were seen no more. 'She's gone!' shouted someone. 'Pray for their souls,' cried the Admiral, 'and bale!'

Morning came again. The great green seas still swept up, over and around us, streaked with foam. The *Pinta* was nowhere. For a while, the wind lessened and we could carry a little sail, then it came on stronger than before. Supporting himself against the mast, the Admiral held out a box from which every man drew lots to choose who should make pilgrimage to the shrines of the saints, should we ever reach Spain. Three lots were cast, and two fell upon the Admiral himself. The sea still raged. We gave ourselves up for lost. The Admiral went to his cabin and there hastily wrote an account of his discoveries which he addressed to the King of Spain; he wrapped it in waxed cloth, put it in a cask and threw it into the sea. Another like it he placed on the poop so that it should float off when we sank. Night came on again, but the third morning found us still afloat.

Many were ill, so ill that they lay unconscious, rolling back and forth with the ship, and in this way one of the Caribs was swept overboard. The crew vowed to Our Lady that every man of them would go in pilgrimage to her shrine at the next land they reached. After a while, the sea calmed a little, the wind abated, and we were able to hoist the mainsail. Then, in the evening, we sighted land.

But the wind had veered against us. All night, the sailors fought towards the land, which some believed to be Spain, others Portugal, but which, when morning came, proved to be no more than a rocky island. Wet, hungry, numb with cold and fatigue, the men could almost have wept. The Admiral limped painfully back to the swamped cabin, the sodden charts, and presently concluded that this was Santa Maria, in the Azores. He was right, as we found later. But for the rest of that day the struggle went on, and not until the next were we able to reach shelter.

The weather was still bad, but the fury of the storm had abated, and for the time being we were not in danger from the sea. Instead, the Admiral was faced with a new difficulty.

Half of the crew, led by Vincent Pinzon, the brother of Martin Alonzo, went ashore in the boat to make their pilgrimage to

Our Lady's chapel, and to pray for the souls of the men who were lost with the *Pinta*. Those remaining were to do likewise when the others returned. But they did not return. Several hours passed, and the Admiral became anxious.

Presently, we saw a crowd of people running down to the shore, many of them armed. A boat put off and started towards us. The Admiral immediately warned his men to arm themselves and keep hidden. There was still a high wind blowing, and it was raining fiercely, and the men crouched with chattering teeth, waiting for the boat.

We Indians were far too ill and wretched to care what further misfortune might be in store for us; least of all did we care for the difference between a Spaniard and a Portuguese. The Admiral, of course, knew well enough that the Azores belong to the Crown of Portugal; he also knew (who better?) how keen was the rivalry between Portugal and Spain for the leadership at sea. What he could not know was that the King of Portugal had had news, a year ago, of this expedition that was setting out to explore the ocean, and had tried every means to intercept it. When his ships had failed, he sent word to the Governor of the Azores, ordering him to detain and capture the Admiral the moment he put in there, should he ever do so. By this means he meant to reserve for Portugal such profits as might come from the discovery of land beyond the sea. But of these developments, as I say, the Admiral was ignorant. He stood above, and watched the armed men coming towards him in the boat.

When they were within hail, their Captain stood up and asked for safe-conduct to come aboard. The Admiral freely granted it. Probably he thought the bird was in the net and, having a hostage, he would be able to demand the return of his men. But unfortunately, when the boat was nearly alongside, one of our crew let his crossbow be seen, and the Portuguese, seeing we were ready armed, thought better of it and sheered off to a safe distance. From there they hailed again, demanding to know if one Christopher Columbus was aboard. The Admiral replied, 'Yes,' and demanded in his turn that they send back his men immediately and unharmed. At this there was a great deal of argument in the boat, and the Captain got up and shouted something which could not be heard clearly, but seemed to imply that we had no right to land on Portuguese territory. The Admiral answered at some length, related our circumstances, made it clear that we had no unfriendly intentions towards Portugal, and was at pains to point out his own rank and standing with the King and Queen of Castile. To this the Captain replied with derision.

'What's that to me!' he bellowed. 'We don't know any King of Castile here!'

The other men started shouting to the same effect, and the Captain finished by commanding the Admiral to come into their boat under arrest, or it would be the worse for all of us. The Admiral's temper was out.

'Unless you send back my men within the hour you shall know the King of Castile sooner than you think,' he shouted. 'I've still enough men aboard to sail my ship, and when I return here I'll hang every skulking lout of a Portuguese in the length and breadth of your whole accursed island!'

For reply, the man merely shrugged and ordered his boat back to the shore. The day went by and the missing crew did not return.

Here was a quandary! For all his words, the Admiral had very few of his best sailors aboard. With the approach of night the rain was coming down in torrents, the wind had changed its quarter and was increasing, and, to make matters worse, the *Niña* began to drag her anchor. We were in danger of being driven ashore. There was nothing for it but to put to sea again.

The Admiral had hoped to find shelter at the neighbouring island of San Miguel, but all that night he was unable to reach it. The storm increased until he had to give up any hope of doing more than ride it out as best he could. Next morning it had abated sufficiently for the sailors to set more sail, but still they could not make headway. Later, the gale spent itself, and the Admiral decided to put back to Santa Maria to try if our fortune would be any better on a second visit.

Luckily it was. Soon after we had returned to the anchorage a boat put out from the shore. This time there were no soldiers, but a deputation headed by two monks and a notary, whom the Admiral permitted to come aboard. They had come, they said, merely to satisfy themselves that his previous statements were true, and to examine his commission from the Sovereigns of Castile. If that were all in order, why, then, his men would be set free without delay and he should continue unmolested. They were very affable. The Admiral showed them everything they requested and they departed quite satisfied, even more affable than before.

After a little more waiting we saw Vincent Pinzon and his companions coming off in their boat. The Admiral glanced at the weather. The sea was still rough, but the wind was moderate and set fair for Spain. As soon as the men were aboard, he clapped on sail and stood away to sea.

'And may it be long before I set eyes on another Portuguese!' he said.

*   *   *   *

The shore party lost no time in relating their adventure. It appeared that when they landed they had been received with a great show of friendship and curiosity by the inhabitants, who accompanied them on their pilgrimage to the chapel. Once inside, however, the doors were shut on them and the building surrounded by an armed guard. The Governor had made the mistake of supposing Vincent Pinzon to be the Admiral, and it was not for some time that he would believe the truth and realize how he had bungled the whole business. Even then, however, he tried to make the best of it, and had sent off a boat's crew to take the Admiral by force or by craft or by what means they could – knowing, however, that in this his chances of success were slight. When the Captain returned with the Admiral's threat he was in as great a quandary as anyone, and when the *Niña* abruptly left her anchorage, he began to fear he might indeed carry them out. No one was more relieved than the Governor to see the ship return again, and he lost no time in putting a good face on matters and packing his now unwelcome prisoners back aboard.

'And may it be long before I set eyes on another Spaniard!' said he.

*   *   *   *

Again, I must point out (Coatta went on) that I understood nothing of all this at the time. I was a poor savage, sick and wretched, and as we drew nearer to the coast of Europe, the more wretched, sick and poor I became. The waves were calmer now, the wind moderate, and the sailors were looking eagerly towards home. But what had we Indians to look for? Promises had been made to us, but these the angry sea had long washed out of mind. Most of us were hardly conscious of anything, except the numb misery of our sickness. We hoped for death, and indeed must have looked like it, for the crew, now that calmer weather had brought relief from their own miseries, began to have concern for ours. The stove had been set going again, at last, and they dried our blankets and brought us hot food and drink. This warmed us, but I, for one, could not keep it down. I remember an old sailor, one José Murela, putting his arm round my shoulder. 'Never mind, Coatta, never mind. All over soon. Home soon. Worst is over.'

Only a few more days, thought the sailors. Home soon! The worst is over.

But again they reckoned without the weather.

With the suddenness of a blow of the fist, a squall came down. The sails, every one of them, were split from top to bottom. The waves rose like mountains and thundered blackly about us. The ship was tossed like a cork. The sailors baled and baled for their lives. The wind screamed so loud that not a shouted word could be heard above it. Never before had the tempest been so furious, never had the sea pounded so hard. The waves dashed together almost over our heads. Every man aboard prayed aloud as he laboured, vowed to make pilgrimage, vowed to do penance. All night it raged, and was raging still with morning. Then, in the midst of it all, the pilot Roldan, struggled his way to the Admiral and shouted in his ear the one word: 'Land!'

Ahead of us a great peak rose up out of the flying spray. It was the Rock of Cintra, at the mouth of the Tagus. And now that they had reached land at last, the sailors must labour to keep from being dashed to pieces against it. They fought to keep it at bay, their only hope being to make for shelter in the river. By some means, how, I cannot guess, they had mended the foresail, and under this we drove at last to harbour in the roads of Portugal.

People had been watching us all the morning from the cliffs and praying for our safety. We learned afterwards that this had been the most stormy winter within living memory, many ships had been lost, others had been held up for weeks together without daring to sail. That we were spared to come to land can only have been by the special Providence of God.

Yet even now the trials of the Admiral were not quite over.
In Portugal, he stood in danger of imprisonment, even, perhaps,
of death. At very least there would be difficulties to overcome in
some shape or form. The ship was closely watched, various
Royal Officers came aboard, and at last came a summons to the
Admiral to visit the King at Valparaiso, his residence near Lisbon.
He shrugged, and went, perhaps not quite expecting to return.
But return he did, after a few days, attended with great ceremony.
The King had been generous, courteous, and wise. No obstacle
was placed in the path of the Admiral's departure when, the weather
clearing at last, he hoisted sail again for Palos.

✻   ✻   ✻   ✻

Two days later, it was the 15th of March, in the year 1493, the
Niña sailed over the bar into Palos harbour and dropped anchor.
The fishermen, who had seen her coming, sailed ahead and
brought the good news to the town. All the bells of Palos were
ringing as she furled her sails. The people were running from their
houses. The harbour was crowded with boats. The Admiral
stood and waved and waved, laughing. I cannot remember that
I had ever seen him laugh before. But everybody was laughing
that morning. . . .

No, I am mistaken; not everybody. There were some who were
asking for this man and that man, and there were many who asked
after the *Pinta*. Three ships had set out less than a year ago.
Only one, the smallest, had returned.

And then there were we, the Indians; we did not laugh. The
crowd jostled aboard so thick that none could move to stare at the
wonders and the Wild Men who had been brought back from the
other side of the world. The Wild Men sat humbly huddled
together as they had huddled together throughout the long,

terrible voyage; the Wild Men were frightened and ill, and very, very tame. A little later they were brought here to La Rabida, whither the Admiral had already gone ahead.

And a little later still (said Coatta), in the evening, the *Pinta* sailed into Palos and dropped anchor.

fellow. But he lived, though for a long time he was too frail to leave the monastery. During that time he became converted and baptized, and in the end he took the tonsure. He now means to go back and work among his own people. An excellent plan.'

'And what became of the others?'

'The others . . . ? Ah, the Indians! Well, as I told you, one of them died. The rest accompanied Columbus to Barcelona, where they were baptized with great ceremony by the Archbishop, before the whole Court. They were made much of for a while, I believe, though what happened to them in the end I can't properly remember. I think one or two of them returned with the Admiral to the Indies; others were probably given by the King to various noblemen. But I don't really know.'

Conversation became general. Francisco Pizarro rose and stretched himself, and observed that it was growing late. Then Gonzalo de Sandoval turned to the monk and asked a question that had suddenly come into his mind.

'Tell me, Father,' he said, 'what became of the garrison at La Navidad? Is anything known?'

Brother Antonio shook his head, slowly and sadly.

'Nothing,' he said. 'Nothing at all.'

He sighed, and after some reflection, continued:

'It was in January that the Admiral left them, and he did not return there until late November. As you can imagine, he had much to keep him in Spain; there was his triumphal reception at Court, business to be done, a fleet to assemble – and it was a very different fleet, this one, from his first! Seventeen ships there were, great and small, and no stint of men to sail in them. They sailed in September, from Cadiz. And even then, when he reached the Indies, he did not go first to Hispaniola, but delayed among the islands. After all, he deemed them safe enough at La Navidad! However, at last he reached the place. It was after dark when he brought his fleet to anchor, and as he could see nothing of the fort, no light nor anything, he fired a signal gun. There was no reply from the shore. He fired again. I have been told that so great was the sense of foreboding throughout the whole fleet, that not a sound could be heard except the echoes of the gun, dying away mournfully among the trees. They waited anxiously till morning, and went ashore to investigate.

'The fort was a ruin, blackened by fire and hollow with decay. Littered everywhere among the weeds were the mildewed relics of habitation; a broken pot, a torn garment, a pen. And there were three graves.'

'And that was all?'

'All. Nothing is known of the men, or what became of them. Somewhere there must be other graves. . . .'

In the silence that followed, Cortés sat tapping his finger on the table, deep in thought.

'I wonder . . .' he said, at length. 'It is possible that some of them may still be alive, to this day. One hears things, now and then. . . . I once heard of a strange fellow who lived among the Indians in Cuba, and was said to be a survivor of La Navidad. At least, that is what he claimed himself, but from all accounts he was not quite right in his head. He would have nothing to do with Europeans, and devoted his life to wandering about from one Indian village to the next, a sort of self-appointed missionary – though what his mission was is more than I can guess. He was known as Brother Mosca. Somebody once pointed him out to me when he came to my estate. A dirty old man, nearly naked, and smoking that vile tobacco. Of course, it may be true what he says. . . . It may be. But I doubt it.'

'And I,' said Pizarro. 'I doubt it strongly.'

'Probably you are right,' said Brother Antonio. 'But then, I have heard so many strange things in my lifetime, and so many of them have proved to be true. It is easier to doubt than to believe. When I was a boy everyone doubted that there was land on the other side of the Ocean; Columbus himself would have doubted, had you told him he was the discoverer of a great Continent that had lain hidden throughout all known history! Yet these things are true. Surely, then, we may believe, if only to comfort ourselves, that a few men escaped from the wreck of La Navidad? At all events, señores, each of them has played his part, whatever it may have been, in one of the greatest adventures that has ever befallen mankind. It is late now, and I see you are weary. But to-morrow morning, in the chapel, we will say Mass for their souls, and for the soul of Christopher Columbus, the Admiral of the Atlantic.'